GUIDE TO
DINOSAURS

GUIDE TO
DINOSAURS

iCR

INSTITUTE FOR CREATION RESEARCH

Dallas, Texas
www.icr.org

Guide to Dinosaurs

First printing: October 2014
Second printing: June 2015

All Scripture quotations are from the New King James Version.

ISBN: 978-1-935587-56-9
Library of Congress Catalog Number: 2014949962

Please visit our website for other books and resources: www.icr.org

Printed in the United States of America.

Contents

Dinosaur Beginnings and History

Dinosaur Fossils and Discoveries

Dinosaur Kinds

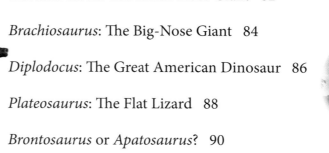

Dinosaur Beginnings and History

Why Study Dinosaurs?

Dinosaurs are fascinating creatures. Seeing them inspires a sense of awe and wonder that sparks the imagination. Whether you are young or young at heart, dinosaurs rarely cease to amaze.

When you think of dinosaurs, you probably imagine the enormous long-necked sauropods or the ferocious *Tyrannosaurus rex*. But dinosaurs came in many different sizes, from as small as a chicken to large enough to reach the tops of tall trees. Some dinosaurs could walk on two feet, while others moved on all four limbs.

As we study dinosaurs we can learn a lot about them, but we also come across many questions. Are dinosaurs mentioned in the Bible? Are they millions of years old? Did humans live at the same time as dinosaurs? Were dinosaurs on the Ark? If they were, how did they all fit? When did God create them? How did dinosaurs go extinct? Did they evolve into birds? These are valid questions, and we will address them and many others in this book.

DINOSAURS CREATED ON DAY 6

The book of Genesis describes how all the animals that moved along the ground, including the dinosaurs, came into existence on Day 6 of the creation week:

> Then God said, "Let the earth bring forth the living creature according to its kind: cattle and creeping thing and beast of the earth, each according to its kind"; and it was so. And God made the beast of the earth according to its kind, cattle according to its kind, and everything that creeps on the earth according to its kind. And God saw that it was good. (Genesis 1:24-25)

The subsequent verses (Genesis 1:26-28) describe the creation of humans and how God gave them (and us) dominion over all the animals He had created, including birds and fish.

The Bible also states that there was no death before Adam and Eve sinned and that the animals were created as herbivores (Genesis 1:29-30). Animals began to eat one another after the Fall, but it is unclear whether this happened gradually or suddenly. Even today, paleontologists have to speculate from dinosaur teeth, jaw structure, and fossil dung as to what dinosaurs ate. Tooth shape alone does not indicate diet since some animals today with sharp teeth (such as fruit bats) are strictly or mostly vegetarian. Many "meat eating" dinosaurs may have remained herbivores, using their sharp teeth to break through the tough skins of fruits and rough exteriors of roots.

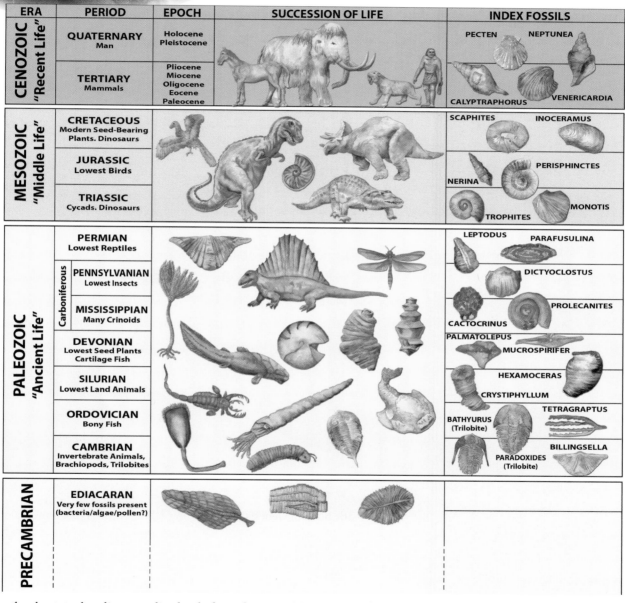

ERA	PERIOD	EPOCH	SUCCESSION OF LIFE	INDEX FOSSILS
CENOZOIC "Recent Life"	QUATERNARY Man	Holocene Pleistocene		PECTEN NEPTUNEA
	TERTIARY Mammals	Pliocene Miocene Oligocene Eocene Paleocene		CALYPTRAPHORUS VENERICARDIA
MESOZOIC "Middle Life"	CRETACEOUS Modern Seed-Bearing Plants. Dinosaurs			SCAPHITES INOCERAMUS
	JURASSIC Lowest Birds			NERINA PERISPHINCTES
	TRIASSIC Cycads. Dinosaurs			TROPHITES MONOTIS
PALEOZOIC "Ancient Life"	PERMIAN Lowest Reptiles			LEPTODUS PARAFUSULINA
	Carboniferous PENNSYLVANIAN Lowest Insects			DICTYOCLOSTUS
	Carboniferous MISSISSIPPIAN Many Crinoids			PROLECANITES CACTOCRINUS
	DEVONIAN Lowest Seed Plants Cartilage Fish			PALMATOLEPUS MUCROSPIRIFER
	SILURIAN Lowest Land Animals			HEXAMOCERAS CRYSTIPHYLLUM
	ORDOVICIAN Bony Fish			BATHYURUS (Trilobite) TETRAGRAPTUS
	CAMBRIAN Invertebrate Animals, Brachiopods, Trilobites			PARADOXIDES (Trilobite) BILLINGSELLA
PRECAMBRIAN	EDIACARAN Very few fossils present (bacteria/algae/pollen?)			

Most textbooks state that dinosaurs lived only from the upper Triassic Period through the Jurassic Period and went extinct at the end of the Cretaceous Period, during a section of time known as the Mesozoic Era supposedly 225 to 65 million years ago. But researchers have found dinosaur bones in rocks even deeper down in middle Triassic rocks in Tanzania. And small dinosaur footprints have been reported in Poland that go deeper still to lower Triassic rocks (presumed to be 250 million years old). The uniformitarian view, which holds that Earth's natural processes weren't much different in the past than they are today, considers that these different strata represent millions of years of deposition. However, these rock layers look more like they were deposited during the year-long Flood that occurred just several thousand years ago. The dinosaurs are found in layers deposited later in the Flood. They are in higher strata since they likely were more mobile and lived at higher elevations than other animals and sea creatures.

What Is a Dinosaur?

The group name Dinosauria was first used by Sir Richard Owen in 1841 in an address to the British Association for the Advancement of Science. He later published the term in 1842. He was the first to recognize that dinosaurs (from Greek words meaning "fearfully great reptile") were a distinct group of reptiles that were different from today's lizards.

Richard Owen

Owen defined dinosaurs as reptiles that walked erect, having a posture similar to elephants and rhinoceroses. He determined this from their hip structure and the holes in the hip sockets. However, there were some early paleontologists who still thought dinosaurs walked in the sprawling, belly-dragging style of modern alligators and crocodiles. Owen's interpretation won the day after further examination of the large rib cages of dinosaurs, which could only fit with long, straight legs. Paleontologists never found belly-dragging marks with dinosaur footprints (with one possible exception where the dinosaurs were mired up to their hips in mud). Instead, they discovered a multitude of dinosaur footprints following narrow trackways.

DID YOU KNOW?

Dinosaurs did not have wings, flippers, or fins. Dinosaurs walked, and occasionally ran, on land. Other reptiles flew or had fins to swim, but they are not classified as dinosaurs.

Another British paleontologist, Harry Seeley, later divided the dinosaurs into two categories based on their hip styles. He called one group the ornithischia (bird-hipped style) and the other the saurischia (lizard-hipped style). All dinosaurs can be classified into one hip style or the other. Although the pelvic bones of the saurischia resemble a lizard, these dinosaurs still had hip sockets for walking upright.

Harry Seeley

Triceratops and *Stegosaurus* had ornithischian dinosaur hips.

Triceratops
try-SEH-ruh-tops

Stegosaurus
STEG-uh-SAWR-us

Allosaurus and the *Di-plodocus* had saurischian dinosaur hips.

Diplodocus
di-PLOD-uh-kus

Allosaurus
AL-oh-SAWR-us

All of the thero-pod dinosaurs (many of which became meat-eaters after the Fall) and the sauropod dinosaurs (the long-necked herbivores) have similar, lizard-style hips. All other types of dino-saurs had bird-style hips. It is rather ironic that the supposedly "bird-like" dinosaurs of the theropod group had lizard-style hips. This shows that they are distinct creatures and that dinosaurs did not evolve into birds as many like to believe.

WHAT ARE NOT DINOSAURS

Other large reptiles lived in the water and flew in the air, but they are not classified as dinosaurs according to Richard Owen's definition. Swim-ming reptiles lived in the ma-rine realm and did not walk or have the hip structures that dinosaurs had. These creatures were perfectly designed for aquatic life.

Ichthyosaurus
ICK-thee-uh-SAWR-us

Mosasaurus
MOS-uh-SAWR-us

Plesiosaurus
PLEE-see-oh-SAWR-us

This fossil shows an ichthyosaur giving live birth in the water and not laying eggs like most reptiles. The mother and her young were quickly buried by fast-moving water and sediment from some type of catastrophic event, like the Flood of Noah's day.

Many extinct sail-backed reptiles, like *Dimetrodon* (which grew to lengths of nearly 10 feet), are similar to lizards we see today because they had sprawling hips and legs that extended outward from their bodies. These animals were not dino-saurs either.

Dimetrodon
dye-MET-ruh-don

Pterodactyl
TARE-oh-DAK-til

Pterosaurs were flying reptiles that were also not dinosaurs. They flew differently than birds or bats. They had an extended system of finger bones, starting with the fourth metacarpal, which was attached to four elongated phalanges that sup-ported a flight membrane made of skin like bats' wings. The remaining three fingers were short claws on the front of the wings.

Dinosaurs in the Bible

The Bible says that God created all the land animals on Day 6 of the creation week, and this would have included the dinosaurs. Genesis 1:25 states, "And God made the beast of the earth according to its kind, cattle according to its kind, and everything that creeps on the earth according to its kind. And God saw that it was good." Some dinosaurs were small and could be categorized as "creeping things," while others were large and fell under the "beast[s] of the earth" category.

The Bible does not contain the word "dinosaur" since it was translated into English centuries before the term existed. However, ancient texts, including the Bible, contain descriptions of creatures that match known dinosaurs.

BEHEMOTH

The book of Job, which is probably the oldest book of the Bible, contains this passage:

> Look now at the behemoth, which I made along with you; He eats grass like an ox. See now, his strength is in his hips, And his power is in his stomach muscles. He moves his tail like a cedar; The sinews of his thighs are tightly knit. His bones are like beams of bronze, His ribs like bars of iron. (Job 40:15-18)

This seems to describe a huge animal with a long neck that ate grass—much like a sauropod such as the *Brachiosaurus* pictured here. Until recently, most secular paleontologists believed that grasses did not exist during the time in which the dinosaurs lived. However, fossilized dinosaur dung (coprolites) from upper Cretaceous rocks of India show that sauropods did eat grass.

Sauropod femur

TANNIN

The term "dragon" appears over 20 times in the Bible, translated into English from the related Hebrew words *tannin* and *tannim*. These words can also be translated as "monster," "serpent," and "sea monster." Psalm 74:13 refers to sea dragons, which could have possibly meant swimming reptiles such as the plesiosaur or mosasaur. Isaiah 30:6 also mentions flying serpents or reptiles, possibly a pterosaur. While those are not dinosaurs according to modern definitions, Isaiah 34 in the King James Version does mention land dragons, which were possibly dinosaurs.

The words "beams of bronze" used to describe the bones of behemoth can also describe dinosaur bones. Sauropods have massive leg bones as thick and strong as metal beams.

Brachiosaurus
BRACK-ee-uh-SAWR-us

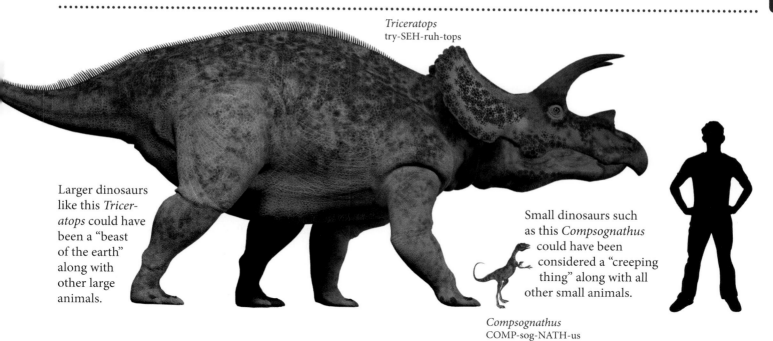

Triceratops
try-SEH-ruh-tops

Larger dinosaurs like this *Triceratops* could have been a "beast of the earth" along with other large animals.

Small dinosaurs such as this *Compsognathus* could have been considered a "creeping thing" along with all other small animals.

Compsognathus
COMP-sog-NATH-us

For unknown reasons, some Bible translators describe behemoth as a hippopotamus or possibly an elephant. But the Bible is clear that behemoth had a "tail like a cedar" (Job 40:17) and was "the first of the ways of God" (Job 40:19), meaning it was very large. Thus, the Bible's description best fits a sauropod.

Elephant

Lebanese Cedar

Hippopotamus

The Pre-Flood Climate

Fossil bones reveal that some dinosaurs grew to huge sizes. How did they grow so big? Studies by uniformitarian scientists suggest there was a very different set of environmental conditions in the past, which creationists apply to the pre-Flood world. Most living things, including dinosaurs, most likely lived on a super-continent. Dinosaurs might have roamed from one end of the land mass to the other, spreading around the world. Creation scientists believe that this land mass broke up during the Flood, separating the continents while Noah and the land animals were protected by God's grace on the Ark.

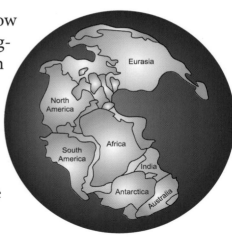

Computer models based on geochemical signatures in the rocks indicate higher carbon dioxide levels in the pre-Flood world (associated with Paleozoic and Mesozoic rocks)—as much as three to seven times today's levels. Many paleontologists also suggest there were higher levels of oxygen, making up as much as 30% of the atmosphere. Not only do geochemical models indicate higher oxygen levels, but the gigantism exhibited by pre-Flood insects and dinosaurs supports this conclusion. Gigantism in various animals has been tied to higher oxygen levels. Higher concentrations of oxygen and carbon dioxide might have helped plants to flourish and animals to grow to the tremendous sizes exhibited by the fossils we find. There was most likely a worldwide greenhouse effect with a warm and moist climate due to the higher oxygen and carbon dioxide levels.

DID YOU KNOW?

During the pre-Flood days, dragonflies had wingspans up to two feet, and some dinosaurs grew to as much as 160 feet long.

The extinction of dinosaurs after the Flood may have been partly caused by rapid changes to the climate and to the atmospheric composition. A significant drop in oxygen concentration to the current 21%, combined with cooler conditions in the north and south latitudes, would have limited the range and possibly slowed the activity levels of dinosaurs, especially if they were cold-blooded.

The dominant plant types were probably different in the pre-Flood world. The warmer climate and atmospheric compositional differences allowed the pteridophytes (seedless vascular plants like ferns) and gymnosperms (naked-seed vascular plants like conifers) to dominate the landscape. Like in today's swamps, there were few flowering plants where dinosaurs would have lived. Scientists have found evidence of ferns and conifers in the stomach regions of hadrosaurs (duck-billed dinosaurs). And scientists have found that sauropods (long-necked dinosaurs) ate grass just like the behemoth in the Bible (Job 40:15), according to fossilized grass remains in their dung.

It is possible that there was no violent weather before the Flood, and the earth may have been watered primarily from below (Genesis 2:6). With oxygen levels as high as 30%, lightning would have caused raging forest fires if they'd had storms like we do today.

God's Post-Flood Promise

God made a post-Flood covenant with Noah and every living creature including dinosaurs that He would never again cause a worldwide flood (Genesis 9:13-17). The sign for that covenant is the rainbow He set in the clouds. Some have argued that the Flood of Noah was a local event only—not global. But if the rainbow was a promise to never again send a local flood upon the earth, God would have broken this promise with every swollen river or tsunami.

Some have suggested the breakup of the supercontinent occurred after the Flood, but this is unlikely. The tremendous tectonic forces and catastrophic volcanic effects of the breakup of a supercontinent would have destroyed much of life on Earth again. Some think the earth was "divided" by language differences at Babel when God scattered mankind over the face of the earth (see Genesis 10:25; 11:9), while others think it was divided by rivers, signifying the end of unstable Ice Age weather patterns.

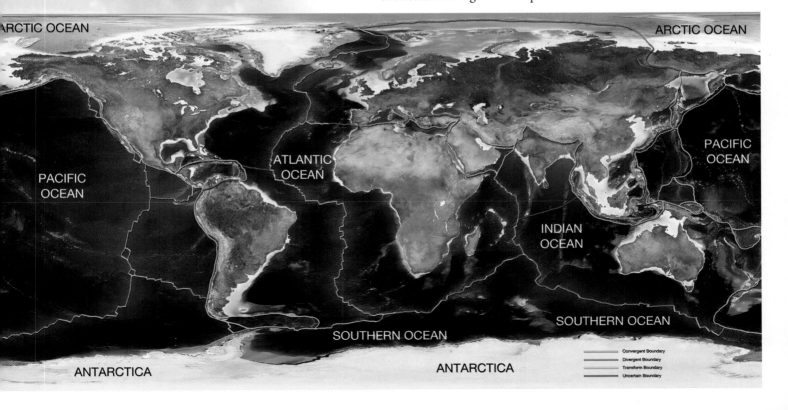

ARCTIC OCEAN

ARCTIC OCEAN

PACIFIC OCEAN

PACIFIC OCEAN

ATLANTIC OCEAN

INDIAN OCEAN

SOUTHERN OCEAN

SOUTHERN OCEAN

ANTARCTICA

ANTARCTICA

Convergent Boundary
Divergent Boundary
Transform Boundary
Uncertain Boundary

Dinosaurs on the Ark

God's world was created "very good." But after humans sinned, the world was corrupted. Eventually the evil became so bad God decided to wipe out most animals and humans and start over with a remnant saved aboard the Ark He told Noah to build. Genesis 6:20 states, "Of the birds after their kind, of animals after their kind, and of every creeping thing of the earth after its kind, two of every kind will come to you to keep them alive." This means that all of the various kinds of dinosaurs were included on the Ark. But how did they fit?

If the biblical "kind" is closer to the "family" in the animal classification we use today, then there were about 60 pairs of dinosaurs on the Ark. (Evolutionary paleontologists recognize around 60 dinosaur families.) In addition, most dinosaur pairs on the Ark would likely have been smaller, youthful, and at the onset of maturity—not the largest and oldest dinosaurs. After all, the purpose of the Ark was to save animal kind representatives that could later repopulate the post-Flood world, and that is best accomplished by young and healthy animals.

Replica dinosaur nest and eggs

BABY DINOSAURS

Dinosaur eggs were relatively small compared to the adults that produced them. The largest known dinosaur eggs are about the size of a football, so dinosaurs were quite small when they were young.

AVERAGE DINOSAUR SIZE ON THE ARK

The median size of dinosaurs was about the size of an American bison. On the Ark, though, the dinosaurs were likely younger than fully mature adults, and their average size was probably closer to that of a sheep. And all dinosaurs experienced a year or two when they grew very rapidly, similar to teenage humans. Dinosaurs were possibly taken onto the Ark about a year prior to this growth spurt. They would've needed less to eat over the course of the year-long Flood so their food needed less space. After the Flood, upon their release to the land, the dinosaurs would have experienced their growth spurt, rapidly maturing to adult size and later able to fulfill God's command to repopulate and fill the earth (Genesis 9:7).

Sheep

Compsognathus
COMP-sog-NATH-us

OTHER YOUNG REPTILES

Dinosaurs were reptiles, so we can look at living reptiles to try and understand more about them. Crocodiles and pythons can grow to enormous sizes and weights. However, when they are young, they are quite small. Once they hit a certain age, they grow rapidly to their adult sizes. Their growth slows down when they are older. Since the dinosaurs on the Ark were needed to repopulate the earth after the great Flood, they would have been young and healthy, and therefore smaller than their massive adult sizes. They would not have taken up much room on the Ark, and the same goes for other animals on board.

Baby python

Baby crocodile

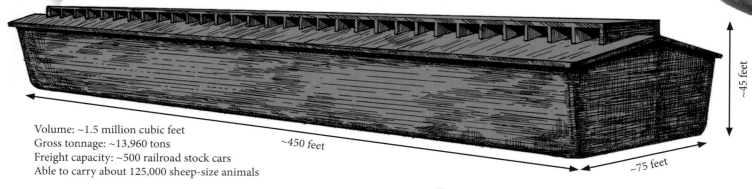

Volume: ~1.5 million cubic feet
Gross tonnage: ~13,960 tons
Freight capacity: ~500 railroad stock cars
Able to carry about 125,000 sheep-size animals

~450 feet

~75 feet

~45 feet

SIZE OF THE ARK

The Ark was very large, according to Genesis 6:15—300 cubits long, 50 cubits wide, and 30 cubits tall. In modern measurements, it would have been about 450 feet long, 75 feet wide, and 45 feet tall. These dimensions were ideally designed for maximum capacity and stability, and a vessel of these dimensions would have been practically impossible to capsize, even in the extremely violent Flood waters. And at this size, the Ark would have provided room for as many as 125,000 sheep-size animals. Only about 25,000 species of land animals (mammals, birds, amphibians, and reptiles) are living today. Because most of these animals are smaller than sheep-size, only about a third the capacity of the Ark would have been needed for animal storage.

Panda

EATING ON THE ARK

The Bible says that God designed all animals to be herbivores in the beginning (Genesis 1:29). Even today, we see animals like pandas with sharp teeth and claws—normally associated with carnivores—that are strict vegetarians. So, all dinosaurs were probably herbivores once, including meat-eating theropods like *T. rex*.

With this in mind, the food stored on the Ark would have been only varieties of plant matter, including fruits, leaves, stalks, roots, and so on. And since the animals on board had to survive the Flood, God would not have allowed them to eat one another. In order to fulfill God's command to multiply and fill the earth, even animals that had become meat-eaters probably ate vegetarian diets during and, for a time, directly after the Flood.

Rising Floodwaters

During the great Flood, the dinosaurs not protected in the Ark would have tried to escape the rising waters for as long as they could. Although most dinosaur footprints found today show dinosaurs walking across muddy ground, there are indications that some tracks were made in shallow water. Discoveries of swimming dinosaurs have been reported from several locations in Europe, Australia, North America, and China.

At the Chinese site, scientists determined at least one dinosaur was partly afloat because it left a 50-foot trail showing tiptoe scratches and claw scrapings along the trackway. A second dinosaur, walking in the same direction and on the same horizon, appeared to wade on the bottom—it left more complete footprints. The similar size of the pair of dinosaurs that left evidence of simultaneous swimming and wading indicates rapid fluctuations in water depth. The consistent direction of the trackways also demonstrates that the dinosaurs were traveling in the same direction, possibly trying to escape the approaching floodwater. A similar discovery was reported at a dinosaur trackway site in Queensland, Australia.

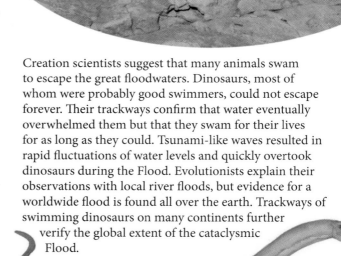

Creation scientists suggest that many animals swam to escape the great floodwaters. Dinosaurs, most of whom were probably good swimmers, could not escape forever. Their trackways confirm that water eventually overwhelmed them but that they swam for their lives for as long as they could. Tsunami-like waves resulted in rapid fluctuations of water levels and quickly overtook dinosaurs during the Flood. Evolutionists explain their observations with local river floods, but evidence for a worldwide flood is found all over the earth. Trackways of swimming dinosaurs on many continents further verify the global extent of the cataclysmic Flood.

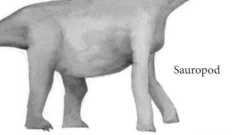

Sauropod

Tracks were made by a sauropod dinosaur like the one above in the limestone along the Paluxy River near Glen Rose, Texas. The tracks were made in soft mud prior to turning to stone and appear to have been covered rapidly during the great Flood, preserving the prints. There are over 100 footprints at the site.

Rocks with ripple marks like these from Grand Canyon tell geologists that they were deposited by moving water. Scientists have found many rippled rocks associated with dinosaur trackways, confirming deposition of the sediments in flowing water. These preserved, delicately rippled surfaces indicate a rapid deposition during the great Flood.

Dinosaurs were forced to start swimming when the flood levels reached their hip height. Prior to that, they could merely wade through the water.

Dinosaur trackways are often found heading in the same direction. Creationists interpret this as the uphill direction away from the rising floodwaters or the direction away from tsunami-like waves generated during the Flood.

The Navajo Sandstone in Utah preserves sandstone layers that are cross-bedded. Flume studies of fast-flowing, sediment-laden water confirm that these layers resulted from giant underwater sand waves generated by tsunami-like events, which creation scientists can attribute to the great Flood.

Dinosaurs in the Ice Age

According to Genesis 6:20, Noah took pairs of every kind of land creature onto the Ark. That means dinosaurs survived the Flood and would have lived during the following Ice Age.

Secular scientists believe Earth experienced at least five major ice ages over millions of years, but they have no real explanation for how even one ice age could have happened, let alone five. The Bible does have an explanation—Noah's Flood. When the "fountains of the great deep" burst open (Genesis 7:11), the resulting volcanic activity heated the oceans and pumped huge amounts of aerosols into the atmosphere, which blocked the sunlight and cooled the high-latitude areas of our planet. This allowed ice sheets to grow until they covered an area about three times the size of today's ice sheets. Over time the earth's volcanic activity settled down, and much of the ice melted.

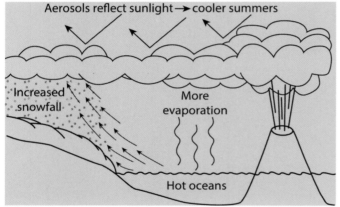

The Flood Caused the Ice Age

Volcanic activity during the Flood heated the world's oceans. After the Flood, these hot oceans resulted in much greater evaporation. The increased moisture caused more snow to fall at higher latitudes and elevations. Residual volcanic activity led to increased aerosols in the atmosphere that reflected large amounts of sunlight. This kept the summers cool enough so the snow wouldn't melt and thick ice sheets could form. As the earth settled down after the Flood, the oceans cooled and fewer volcanic eruptions occurred, leading to the end of the Ice Age.

Where Did Dinosaurs Live?

During the Ice Age, ice sheets began to grow outward from the northern and southern polar regions, pushing people and animals closer to the equator. The Ice Age storms that brought heavy snowfall in the higher latitudes also caused plentiful rains near the equator. Areas in the Middle East and Africa that are desert today would have been quite tropical. Along with the other animals from the Ark, dinosaurs would have thrived in the lush, green lands. When the area dried out after the Ice Age, the dinosaurs would have lost their habitats there.

Did you know?

There was only one Ice Age, and it lasted about 500 years.

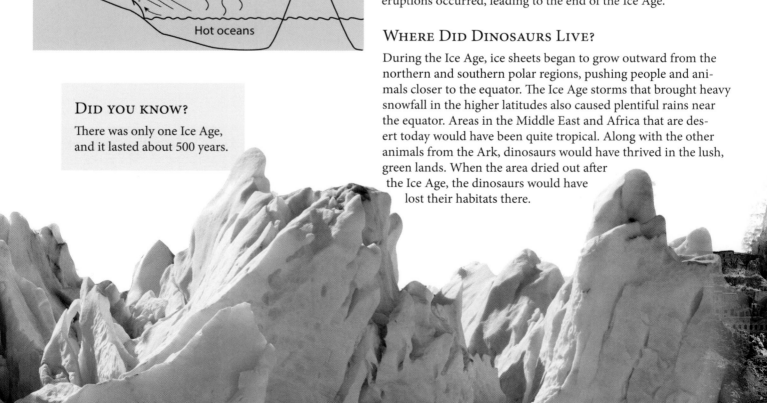

SPREADING OVER THE EARTH

Legends of dinosaur-like creatures (often called dragons) have been found all over the world. How did dinosaurs get to these places after the Flood? Genesis 9:2 says that the fear of man was instilled in animals right after they left the Ark, and this caused dinosaurs to migrate away from human settlements. As ice sheets grew during the Ice Age, they captured massive amounts of the world's water. Sea levels dropped hundreds of feet, exposing land bridges that are submerged today. This allowed dinosaurs and other creatures to spread around the globe.

DID YOU KNOW?

Before the Flood, animals weren't afraid of people the way they are today. But after the Flood, God said, "And the fear of you and the dread of you shall be on every beast of the earth, on every bird of the air, on all that move on the earth, and on all the fish of the sea" (Genesis 9:2).

DINOSAUR ENCOUNTERS

As people scattered across the earth after the Tower of Babel, they would have run across dinosaurs that had migrated to those areas before them. These dinosaur encounters apparently went on for centuries during and after the Ice Age, and this is where many of the legends of dragons likely came from. The Middle East has written dinosaur legends like Bel and the dragon, and St. George and the dragon. Europe and the Far East also have many records of dragon encounters.

TOWER OF BABEL

God commanded Noah's family to "fill the earth" after the Flood, but Genesis 11 tells us that the people disobeyed and stayed together near where the Ark landed. They began building a large tower to honor themselves. This angered God, and He scrambled their language, forcing them to spread out over the earth during the Ice Age. These people would have encountered dinosaurs as they colonized the world.

Encounters with Dragons

Dinosaurs migrated with other animals to various parts of the world after the end of the Flood of Noah's day, and their populations grew. Later, when humans migrated after the events at Babel (Genesis 11), they came across these animals and memorialized the encounters in writings, art, and oral traditions that have been passed down from generation to generation.

Long before the word "dinosaur" existed, people called these large land reptiles a variety of names, including monsters, serpents, and dragons. A multitude of dragon legends is found all over the world and throughout history. Dragons have also been reported by people such as Alexander the Great (356-323 B.C.), John of Damascus (675-749 A.D.), and Marco Polo (1254-1324). Ancient historians, including Josephus (first century A.D.) and Herodotus (fourth century B.C.), also mentioned dragons or winged serpents. Petroglyphs (carvings in stone) and pictographs (paintings on stone) occasionally show creatures that strongly resemble dinosaurs, created by native tribes especially in the Southwestern region of the United States.

Alexander the Great

The Macedonian king Alexander III (356-323 B.C.), also known as Alexander the Great, reportedly saw a hissing dragon in a cave after he and his armies invaded India in 326 B.C.

Marco Polo

Marco Polo (1254-1324) was a traveling merchant from Venice who documented many of his exploratory trips into China, Persia, Burma, and Tibet in a book titled *The Travels of Marco Polo*. During his travels, he recorded seeing a variety of animals, including huge "serpents" that had short legs, claws, and large jaws with sharp teeth. While the description may sound like crocodiles at first, Polo wrote that these creatures only had two short legs near the front of their bodies—not four legs like crocodiles. These animals could have been dinosaurs.

Dinosaur Petroglyph?

This petroglyph at Kachina Bridge in Natural Bridges National Monument in Utah appears to depict a sauropod.

CHINESE ZODIAC

The Chinese zodiac features 12 animals, including a dragon that is supposedly the only mythological creature used. For the nations that have used this zodiac system for millennia, why would they include 11 real animal representations like the horse, rabbit, and monkey, and one "unreal" creature? The Chinese zodiac also features a snake, which shows that the ancient people who developed it knew the difference between dragons and other reptiles. It is likely that they encountered dinosaurs in the past, called them dragons, and included them on the zodiac.

NARMER PALETTE

An ancient Egyptian plaque known as the Narmer Palette depicts humans handling two creatures that resemble long-necked dinosaurs. The animals on the plaque have legs that extend straight down from their bodies and serpentine necks—two features found in sauropod dinosaurs.

STEGOSAURUS CARVING ON CAMBODIAN TEMPLE WALL

This carving at the Ta Prohm temple near the province of Siem Reap in Cambodia dates back to the 1100s. It depicts a *Stegosaurus* carved nearly 800 years before scientists discovered fossil bones of such a creature.

Dinosaur Extinction

No dinosaurs are known to live in our world today. Their remains are found on every continent on Earth, and they seem to have died out suddenly, along with many other species. What happened to them?

Dozens of theories have tried to explain dinosaur extinction. Most scientists believe they died at the end of the Cretaceous Period because of a catastrophic global event such as a giant asteroid smashing into the earth or a dramatic change in the climate. But the popular asteroid-extinction theory doesn't work because an event violent enough to kill off the dinosaurs would also have wiped out the more vulnerable species like mammals and amphibians. The climate change theories—which involve either severe cold or excessive heat—also fail as an explanation because these now-extinct creatures would have likely migrated and survived in the parts of the world that were less affected by the weather patterns.

What else could have caused the death and burial of billions of creatures? How about a global flood?

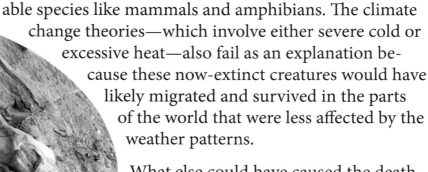

FOSSIL GRAVEYARDS

When dinosaur bones are unearthed, they are often found in vast fossil graveyards. These bone beds are located all over the world. The bones are tightly packed together and are powerful evidence for a global flood since the fossils they contain are buried in vast layers of sedimentary rock that was once watery mud. The dinosaurs are often found mixed together with a variety of other creatures, demonstrating that all these life forms died at the same time and were buried rapidly before they could decay or be scavenged.

Megalosaurus
MEG-uh-luh-SAWR-us

POWERFUL FORCES

The largest dinosaurs weighed many tons, yet the ones found in fossil graveyards were overcome by forces so powerful that even these great creatures could not escape. Young dinosaurs are almost never found in fossil graveyards, and this indicates that these creatures were likely under stress and on the run when they were entombed in the muddy water. There is little question that a cataclysmic event happened—the global Flood.

WHAT ABOUT THE DINOSAURS ON THE ARK?

There were dinosaurs on Noah's Ark, so these creatures obviously survived the Flood. Why did their descendants die out while so many other mammal, reptile, and amphibian species survived? After the Tower of Babel, humans began to spread across the globe, following the same Ice Age land bridges used earlier by migrating animals. As humans settled new areas, they would have encountered a variety of animals, including dinosaurs. Any animal threat to the people's safety would have been met with quick, violent action. Humans would have also hunted large species for food. Dragon legends and historical records suggest that some dinosaurs survived into the Middle Ages, but unless some remnant still exists in a remote, isolated location, dinosaurs no longer roam the earth.

Theropod footprint

LOSS OF HABITAT

As the Ice Age ended, the oceans cooled and volcanic activity diminished, leading to fewer snow and rainstorms. The land around the equator in the Middle East and Africa began to dry out, forcing dinosaurs to leave these formerly tropical areas. Climate changes from rising seas, melting snows, and droughts—not to mention the spreading human population—likely contributed to the loss of suitable habitats. All of this would have affected the dwindling number of dinosaurs on the earth after the Flood.

DID YOU KNOW?

Dinosaur tracks are found in over 1,500 locations around the globe! Most of these dinosaur footprints were made during the Flood as the dinosaurs tried to outrun rising floodwaters and make their way to higher ground.

Dinosaurs and the Problem of Death

If evolution is true, there had to be millions of years of death in order for earlier life forms to slowly evolve into more complex and advanced creatures.

But according to the Bible, death and evil entered the world only after man's sin. God told Adam, "Cursed is the ground for your sake; In toil you shall eat of it….Till you return to the ground" (Genesis 3:17, 19). Adam and Eve's sin also cut off their relationship with God and required Him to send a Savior to redeem not only them, but us as well.

So where dinosaurs came from and how long ago they lived aren't just interesting questions. If death existed before Adam, then death wasn't the result of sin. And if it wasn't, then Christ's death on the cross wasn't necessary because it couldn't have paid the penalty for sin. And if the penalty wasn't paid, then we are still cut off from God. In evolution's story about dinosaurs, there is no room for God's redemption. But in the Bible's history, we have the hope that only Christ can give!

DID YOU KNOW?

There was no death before Adam sinned. "Through one man sin entered the world, and death through sin, and thus death spread to all men, because all sinned" (Romans 5:12).

A VEGETARIAN DIET

Dinosaurs and other animals were vegetarians before the Fall. God said in Genesis 1:30, "To every beast of the earth, to every bird of the air, and to everything that creeps on the earth, in which there is life, I have given every green herb for food." This was true for humans, too. It wasn't until after the Flood that God allowed people to eat meat. He told Noah, "Every moving thing that lives shall be food for you. I have given you all things, even as the green herbs" (Genesis 9:3).

NO FOSSILS BEFORE ADAM

Evolutionists believe humans arrived millions of years after the first living organisms evolved, so they think that most of the fossil record developed before we even got here. But since there was no death until Adam sinned, no fossils could have formed before him because fossils can only be made from dead animals and plants. God created everything perfect and fully formed, and most of the fossils we find were made during the great Flood of Noah's day—including the giant dinosaur fossils we see in museums.

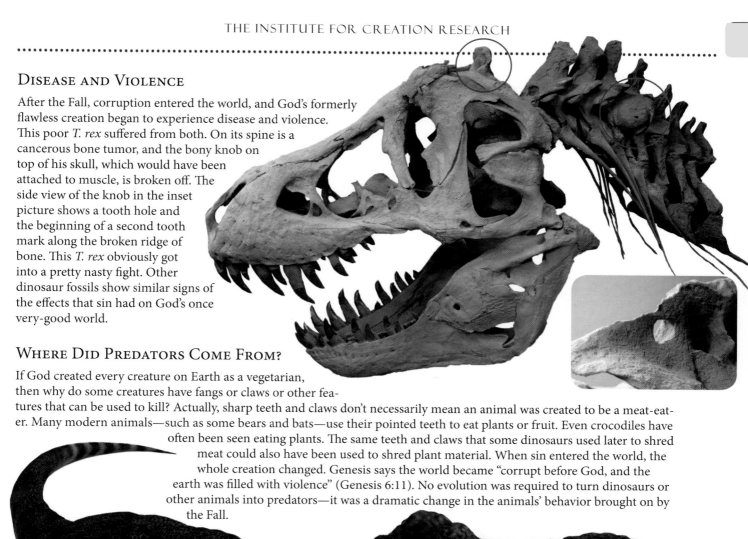

DISEASE AND VIOLENCE

After the Fall, corruption entered the world, and God's formerly flawless creation began to experience disease and violence. This poor *T. rex* suffered from both. On its spine is a cancerous bone tumor, and the bony knob on top of his skull, which would have been attached to muscle, is broken off. The side view of the knob in the inset picture shows a tooth hole and the beginning of a second tooth mark along the broken ridge of bone. This *T. rex* obviously got into a pretty nasty fight. Other dinosaur fossils show similar signs of the effects that sin had on God's once very-good world.

WHERE DID PREDATORS COME FROM?

If God created every creature on Earth as a vegetarian, then why do some creatures have fangs or claws or other features that can be used to kill? Actually, sharp teeth and claws don't necessarily mean an animal was created to be a meat-eater. Many modern animals—such as some bears and bats—use their pointed teeth to eat plants or fruit. Even crocodiles have often been seen eating plants. The same teeth and claws that some dinosaurs used later to shred meat could also have been used to shred plant material. When sin entered the world, the whole creation changed. Genesis says the world became "corrupt before God, and the earth was filled with violence" (Genesis 6:11). No evolution was required to turn dinosaurs or other animals into predators—it was a dramatic change in the animals' behavior brought on by the Fall.

DID YOU KNOW?

Predators need to learn how to hunt and kill. They are not born with the skills to be successful hunters—they must learn how to kill from their parents or the animals in their pack or pride.

Dinosaur Myths

Scientists have learned a lot about dinosaurs in the years since Charles Darwin published his *Origin of Species,* and they are learning more all the time. But in addition to all the good scientific information that is available about these fascinating reptiles, there are misinformation and wrong assumptions that cloud what the evidence really shows. Here are just a few of the stories that have affected how people understand the history and lives of dinosaurs.

PALUXY RIVER TRACKS

The Paluxy River near Glen Rose, Texas, is famous for its dinosaur tracks. Along with the prints of recognizable dinosaurs, tracks were found that had an elongated, humanlike shape. Many people took this as evidence proving that dinosaurs and humans co-existed. Over time, though, the tracks have eroded, and it now seems unlikely that they were made by humans. Many of them developed "ghost" overprints that had a three-toed dinosaurian shape with a distinctive rust color. A dinosaur print site in Australia also has humanlike shapes in the center of three-toed prints, indicating the presence of a central "pad" that loosely resembles a human foot. But even if the Paluxy River tracks don't show humans walking alongside dinosaurs, there is still plenty of other evidence that supports the Genesis account that both were created on the same day.

WHERE ARE THE HUMAN FOSSILS?

Some people say that if humans and dinosaurs lived at the same time, then human fossils should be found with dinosaur fossils. But would this be true? The vast majority of fossils are marine creatures. Land creatures have a lower fossilization potential, and a flood that was powerful enough to bury creatures in layers of sediment would have been destructive enough to tear apart fragile mammal bodies. Most of those bodies would have floated and not been buried at all, and others would have been buried late in the Flood. Their fossils would be near the surface and would have been subject to erosion and destruction when the floodwaters rushed off the rising continents. And humans and dinosaurs probably lived in different areas, so the Flood's waves that overwhelmed and buried dinosaurs wouldn't necessarily have swept away humans at the same time. The lack of human fossils is actually more of a problem for evolution. If humans have lived on Earth for hundreds of thousands or millions of years, where are *their* fossils? There should be billions of human fossils instead of just a handful.

TRANSITIONAL FORMS

Evolution says all living creatures evolved from common ancestors through a series of small changes over a very long period of time. That means there should be lots of evidence of transitional creatures—but there isn't. Many fossil finds have been described as "missing links," but each has proved to be a problem for evolutionists to fit into an evolutionary tree. One such find was "Ida." In 2009 she was widely proclaimed to be an evolutionary link in human evolution, but she was almost immediately debunked as an extinct lemur. For every evolutionary scientist who describes a dinosaur or other fossil as a transition, there's another scientist who disagrees. The missing links are still missing.

ARCHAEOPTERYX

One famous "transitional form" is *Archaeopteryx*, which has been portrayed as an evolutionary link between dinosaurs and birds. Although it has unique characteristics such as a long, narrow tail and teeth in its beak, it doesn't have anything that looks like a transitional feature. There are no half-scales/half-feathers, just fully formed flight feathers like modern birds have. It also has other core bird features like wings, perching feet, and a wishbone. Many scientists now agree that *Archaeopteryx* is exactly what it seems to be—an extinct bird. But textbooks and museums still call it a missing link.

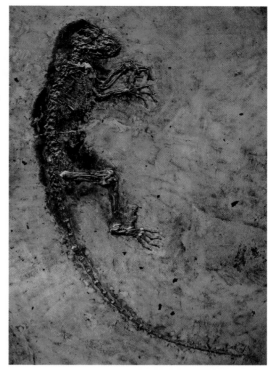

Ida

DESIGNED FEATURES

If evolution is true, a lot of dinosaurs would have had features "in between" the creature they came from and the one they were becoming. But the fossil record does not show this. Instead, each dinosaur is amazingly complex, with every body part precisely designed to perform the exact function the dinosaur needed. And all the parts had to be there at the same time or the dinosaur wouldn't have been able to function at all. For example, many dinosaurs had dense, solid vertebrae. The sauropod, however, had lightweight vertebrae with depressions, raised ridges, and hollowed places. If it had the same dense neck bones as other dinosaurs, it wouldn't have been able to lift its head to reach the trees that provided its food. It would have starved to death! Dinosaur evolution is a myth.

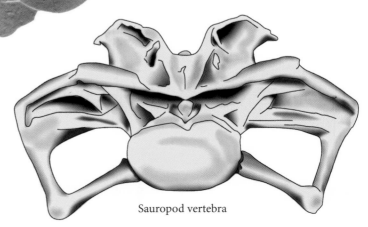

Archaeopteryx
ARK-ee-OP-ter-ix

Sauropod vertebra

Expeditions to the Gobi Desert have produced some of the most spectacular dinosaur fossil finds, including the first recognizable dinosaur eggs.

Dinosaur Fossils and Discoveries

Fossils

The study of fossils is called paleontology. It is similar in some respects to archaeology, but archaeology concentrates on human artifacts, like pottery and Egyptian mummies. Fossils rarely form today, yet there are billions of fossils scattered all around the world. How, then, are things fossilized?

The most important condition is a rapid burial, because it prevents scavenging and helps preserve the remains. But, a rather deep burial is also needed to limit the oxygen supply and slow decay. Thus, catastrophic activity seems to be necessary to form fossils, and the Flood of Noah's day would have definitely provided enough energy to rapidly and deeply bury the fossilized creatures we find today.

TYPES OF FOSSILS

Most fossils can be categorized as 1) petrification (which includes permineralization and replacement), 2) preservation, 3) carbonization, 4) molds and casts, and 5) trace fossils.

PETRIFICATION

In petrification the original organism turns to stone, which usually involves the removal of the majority of the organic material (i.e., muscle tissues, blood vessels, etc.). Groundwater typically dissolves away the original parts while simultaneously depositing inorganic minerals and preserving many of the details of the dead organism. These deposits, such as quartz and pyrite, leave behind exact replicas of the fossil for geologists to study. This process can begin in as few as 80 days under the right conditions.

PRESERVATION

This type of fossil retains original organic parts. Preserved fossils are less common, but scientists continue to find more preserved dinosaur soft tissues. Even the enamel in dinosaur teeth may be preserved. Preserved soft tissue has been found in several dinosaur specimens, including sauropod embryos and blood vessels in the leg bone of a *T. rex*.

T. rex tooth

MOLDS AND CASTS

Molds and casts are the impressions or "shapes" in which the actual organism dissolves away, leaving only its imprint in the rock. Internal molds give the inside imprint of an organism, and external molds give the imprint of the outside of the organism. Dinosaur skin imprints are a type of external mold. Casts are a secondary process in which a mold must first be created by dissolution of the original shell or bone and the cavity is filled in with sediment or other minerals.

CARBONIZATION

Carbonized fossils are typically formed from plants. Carbonization is less common in dinosaurs, but there have been some reports of dinosaur internal organs preserved as carbon residue. It forms when buried organic material "cooks" or distills and leaves behind a thin, black carbon residue.

Fossil ammonite

Fossil fern

TRACE FOSSILS

Trace fossils include tracks, burrows, trails, and anything else that indicates the activity of an organism but without being a direct part of the organism. Other trace fossils include coprolites (fossilized dung) and gastroliths (gizzard stones), which helped some dinosaurs digest their food.

Ornithopod tracks

How Dinosaurs Get Their Names

Dinosaur paleontologists use the same name classification system used in biology. The Linnaean Hierarchy, established by the Swedish naturalist Carolus Linnaeus in the 18th century, is used for all extinct and living organisms. Linnaeus developed this system in an attempt to delineate the "kinds" referred to in the book of Genesis. He believed that there could be limited variation within a kind but that the kinds could not change from one kind to another.

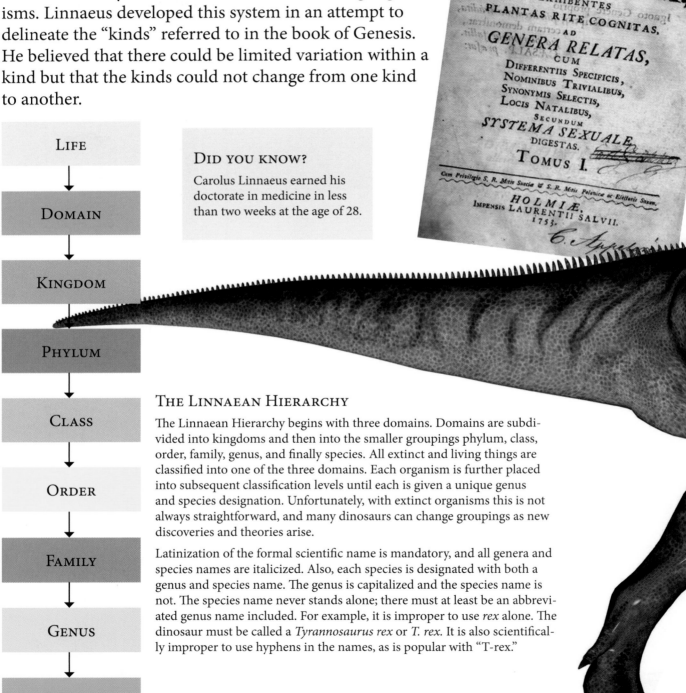

LIFE

↓

DOMAIN

↓

KINGDOM

↓

PHYLUM

↓

CLASS

↓

ORDER

↓

FAMILY

↓

GENUS

↓

SPECIES

DID YOU KNOW?

Carolus Linnaeus earned his doctorate in medicine in less than two weeks at the age of 28.

THE LINNAEAN HIERARCHY

The Linnaean Hierarchy begins with three domains. Domains are subdivided into kingdoms and then into the smaller groupings phylum, class, order, family, genus, and finally species. All extinct and living things are classified into one of the three domains. Each organism is further placed into subsequent classification levels until each is given a unique genus and species designation. Unfortunately, with extinct organisms this is not always straightforward, and many dinosaurs can change groupings as new discoveries and theories arise.

Latinization of the formal scientific name is mandatory, and all genera and species names are italicized. Also, each species is designated with both a genus and species name. The genus is capitalized and the species name is not. The species name never stands alone; there must at least be an abbreviated genus name included. For example, it is improper to use *rex* alone. The dinosaur must be called a *Tyrannosaurus rex* or *T. rex*. It is also scientifically improper to use hyphens in the names, as is popular with "T-rex."

Tyrannosaurus rex means "tyrant lizard king."
tye-RAN-uh-SAWR-us rex

CAROLUS LINNAEUS

Carolus Linnaeus (1707-1778) was a naturalist who was born in Sweden. He later traveled to the Netherlands and earned his doctorate in medicine. Afterward, he returned to Sweden and in 1753 published his two-volume, 1,200-page book titled *Species Plantarum*, which established the modern binomial (two-name) system for living organisms. He was knighted by the king of Sweden that same year and ennobled in 1761, taking the name Carl von Linne.

NAMING NEW DINOSAURS

It is fairly easy to name a new dinosaur. One merely looks down a list of Greek and/or Latin root words and finds one that describes a particular feature about the new specimen for the genus. "Tyranno" means tyrant, for example. A second Greek or Latin root word is added, such as "saurus," which means lizard or reptile.

The species name can honor the discoverer or someone affiliated with the discovery, but it must be Latinized too. Paleontologists digging in Madagascar found a new dinosaur they named *Masiaka-saurus knopfleri,* which means "vicious lizard knopfler," for singer/songwriter Mark Knopfler of the band Dire Straits, which the scientists were listening to as they dug and made the discovery. Another team of researchers found a dinosaur skull with spiky, dragon-like horns in South Dakota's Hell Creek Formation. They named the creature *Dracorex hog-wartsia* in honor of the school in the famous Harry Potter books by J. K. Rowling.

Dracorex hogwartsia
DRAY-coh-rex hog-WART-see-uh

The First Discoveries

Dragon sightings have occurred for millennia, and Chang Qu wrote about "dragon" bones found in what is now Sichuan Province, China, around 300 B.C. Had he written about them today, they would probably have been called dinosaur bones. But the first "official" dinosaurs were not named and described until relatively recently. The first drawing and description of a dinosaur bone in scientific literature was by University of Oxford clergyman and chemist Robert Plot in 1677. He believed the specimen, which was found near Oxfordshire, was from a modern elephant brought to Britain by the Romans. The original specimen was lost, but we now believe it was part of the femur of a theropod dinosaur called *Megalosaurus*.

Robert Plot

WILLIAM BUCKLAND AND *MEGALOSAURUS*

Megalosaurus also became the first dinosaur named and described by William Buckland, a reverend who was also from the University of Oxford. Buckland obtained several teeth and a jaw fragment around 1815 near Stonesfield, Oxfordshire, and passed them by numerous people—including the French anatomist Georges Cuvier—before publishing the name *Megalosaurus* and its description in 1824. *Megalosaurus* was the same name given to the dinosaur by an English surgeon named James Parkinson in 1822, but he had failed to provide a description.

Megalosaurus
MEG-uh-luh-SAWR-us

William Buckland

GIDEON MANTELL AND *IGUANODON*

The first herbivorous dinosaur to be identified was named *Iguanodon* in 1825 by a contemporary of William Buckland, a physician named Gideon Mantell. Mantell and his wife, Mary Ann, reportedly found a few teeth and bones near Sussex, England, in 1822. He also found fragments from three other extinct reptiles (later identified as dinosaurs) in 1833. Unfortunately, most of the dinosaurs found and named in England in the 19th century were fragmentary, and early reconstructions of *Iguanodon* placed its thumb spike on the tip of the snout like a rhinoceros horn. Even today, there are few specimens found in England, and it is a wonder that Richard Owen, who came up with the term "dinosaur," was able to define an extinct group of reptiles from such incomplete evidence.

Iguanodon
ig-WAN-uh-DON

Gideon Mantell

Mantell's inaccurate *Iguanodon* drawing

Hadrosaurus
HAD-roh-SAWR-us

JOSEPH LEIDY AND *HADROSAURUS*

Joseph Leidy was a professor of anatomy at the University of Pennsylvania, and he described the first dinosaurs found in the United States. Leidy named the *Hadrosaurus* in 1858 from a collection of bones found by W. P. Foulke near Haddonfield, New Jersey. In 1856, Leidy had identified a few teeth from Montana as being from a dinosaur, the first discovered in the Western Hemisphere. British sculptor Benjamin Waterhouse Hawkins mounted the bones of the *Hadrosaurus* in 1868 at the Academy of Natural Sciences in Philadelphia.

Joseph Leidy

THE FIRST DINOSAUR FOOTPRINTS

The first known dinosaur footprint was discovered by a teenager, Pliny Moody, in 1802 while he was plowing a field in New England. Because dinosaurs were not understood at the time, the significance of his discovery went largely unnoticed until much later. Some of the earliest work on dinosaur footprints was done by Edward Hitchcock in the mid-19th century. Unfortunately, most scientists of the time were caught up in the search for dinosaur bones, and their footprints were neglected until more recently.

The Great Dinosaur Rush

The Great Dinosaur Rush of the 1870s through the 1890s was fueled by competition between two rival scientists, Edward Drinker Cope and Othniel Charles Marsh. Cope was from a wealthy Philadelphia family who had made a substantial fortune in shipping. Marsh, whose uncle was the millionaire banker George Peabody, was from New York. Cope never earned a formal college degree, but Marsh graduated from Yale and obtained a master's degree from Sheffield Scientific School in 1862. The two first met in Berlin in 1863. In 1869, Cope and Marsh had a disagreement over the remains of a marine reptile called *Elasmosaurus*. This began a 30-year-long competition called the Bone Wars—also known as the Great Dinosaur Rush—that would drain their financial resources as they raced to find the most new species.

Othniel Charles Marsh (center, back row) and his assistants

Edward Drinker Cope (third from right) at the 1896 Buffalo meeting of the American Association for the Advancement of Science

Cope and Marsh often hired competing crews of dinosaur hunters to scour the American West, searching for quarries containing newer finds. Some crews sent a few sample specimens back to each scientist and later submitted the rest of the bones to the highest bidder—who was usually Marsh. These crews developed excavation techniques that are still used today by modern dinosaur hunters. Unfortunately, in their haste and fierce competition, some quarries were destroyed by rival crews, and mistakes were often made in naming new species. Many famous dinosaur quarries were opened, including ones near Como Bluff, Wyoming; Morrison, Colorado; and Cañon City, Colorado. From this feud came some of the most famous dinosaur genera, such as *Apatosaurus, Stegosaurus*, and *Triceratops*. In the end, Marsh also helped establish the foundations for the dinosaur classification system still in use, including the suborders of sauropods, theropods, and ornithopods.

George Peabody and the Peabody Museum of Natural History

PEABODY MUSEUM

Marsh convinced his uncle George Peabody to make a large donation to Yale University in 1863 to establish the Peabody Museum of Natural History. He also used this donation to gain favor with the college. In 1866, he was named the chair of paleontology at Yale University, funded again by his uncle. Marsh holds the record for the most dinosaur genera named and discovered.

HOW THE BONE WARS STARTED

In 1869, Cope invited Marsh to view his recently constructed skeleton of *Elasmosaurus platyrus* at the Academy of Natural Sciences in Philadelphia. The 35-foot-long swimming reptile was only the second reconstructed skeleton of an ancient reptile in the United States, after the dinosaur *Hadrosaurus*. Marsh said that Cope had put the head on the tail, and the feud began. They called in Joseph Leidy, a medical doctor who was considered the American expert in paleontology, who confirmed that Cope had indeed made a mistake. Cope had already published his find with the reptile's skull mounted incorrectly, and he quickly tried to buy back all the journal articles detailing his mistake. However, his reputation was permanently damaged.

Cope was constantly thwarted by Marsh after this mistake, but he did publish over 1,400 papers in his lifetime—still a scientific record, even though many of those papers were self-published at his own expense. He named many other species besides dinosaurs, including fish, lizards, and mammals. Later in life, Cope had to sell much of his fossil collection, at a fraction of his costs, to make ends meet. Cope was also convinced that his brain was bigger than Marsh's. Upon his death, Cope's brain was weighed and measured, but when Marsh passed away two years later, he left instructions to make sure his skull remained intact.

Elasmosaurus
ee-LAS-muh-SAWR-us

BRONTOSAURUS

Marsh named the *Brontosaurus* in 1879, but his specimen had no head, which is a common problem with sauropod dinosaur fossils. He found a different head from miles away and placed it on his reconstructed skeleton. Eventually, paleontologists recognized this was the wrong head and came from a similar-size *Camarasaurus*.

Camarasaurus skull
kuh-MARE-uh-SAWR-us

TRICERATOPS

Marsh named the genus *Triceratops* using a skull discovered by John Bell Hatcher in 1888 in the Judith River Formation in Montana. Marsh initially ignored the first skulls of this genera he came across, confusing the well-preserved remains with those of modern bison.

Triceratops skull

Triceratops
try-SEH-ruh-tops

Dinosaur Hunters

After Edward Drinker Cope and Othniel Charles Marsh, the next generation of dinosaur hunters included Henry Fairfield Osborn, Barnum Brown, and Charles Sternberg. Osborn started New York's American Museum of Natural History's paleontology department in 1897. The museum had previously purchased Cope's fossil collection for $32,000, and Osborn was determined to make the museum a major home for dinosaur fossils. He hired fossil hunters such as Barnum Brown and Charles Sternberg to collect specimens for his museum. Osborn's employees dug at Como Bluff, Wyoming, and found 517 specimens in seven years, including many *Apatosaurus, Camarasaurus,* and *Diplodocus* specimens.

Barnum Brown (left) and Henry Fairfield Osborn (right) at Como Bluff during the American Museum of Natural History expedition of 1897. At front is a limb bone of *Diplodocus.*

Tyrannosaurus rex
tye-RAN-uh-SAWR-us rex

BARNUM BROWN

Barnum Brown was on a summer dig in Wyoming in 1895 when he found his first dinosaur fossil—a *Triceratops* skull. The American Museum of Natural History hired him during the summer of 1897 for a similar dig in Wyoming. Brown found the first specimen of *Tyrannosaurus rex* in 1902—which Osborn named and described in 1905—and a second *T. rex* skeleton in 1908. Brown went on to become one of the most prolific dinosaur hunters of all time and continued to collect for the American Museum throughout his career.

In 1908, Charles Sternberg and his sons found the mummified *Edmontosaurus* pictured at right. It was preserved so well that it still had its skin and abdomen, including the stomach contents of pine needles, twigs, seeds, and roots.

Morrison Formation

THE MORRISON FORMATION

Dinosaur hunters, mostly working for Edward Drinker Cope or Othniel Charles Marsh, opened numerous quarries in the Morrison Formation during the 1870s through the 1890s. The Morrison Formation is located in the western region of the United States, and it is one of the few rock units that keep the same name from state to state rather than being named differently in each state. It was named after Morrison, Colorado, where Arthur Lakes and Henry Beck discovered dinosaur bones while surveying the area on March 26, 1877. They sent bone samples to Marsh and Cope, and Marsh wrote back first, offering $100 a month to begin quarrying. Lakes opened the Morrison quarry later that year, and the discovery of *Apatosaurus* and *Stegosaurus* specimens followed shortly afterward. Other quarries where crews found dinosaurs include sites in Colorado, Utah, and Wyoming.

Dinosaur National Monument Quarry in the Morrison Formation

COMO BLUFF, WYOMING

Part of the Morrison Formation in Como Bluff, Wyoming, contained so many dinosaur bones that a 19th-century sheepherder used about 26,000 fossil bones to build a cabin. Diggers at Como Bluff found fossils of fish, frogs, lizards, turtles, crocodiles, pterodactyls, and mammals mixed in with dinosaurs. Finds like these show that dinosaurs and pterodactyls lived at the same time as currently living creatures like mammals, fish, and frogs. Other formations have dinosaurs and birds mixed together, showing that dinosaurs did not evolve into birds, which is a popular but unobserved theory.

CHARLES STERNBERG

Charles Sternberg began collecting fossils with the support of Cope in the 1870s. While digging in Montana in 1876, the two developed the use of plaster of Paris and burlap strips to encase the fossil bones and protect them during shipment. Sternberg worked for the American Museum of Natural History for part of his career but spent more time as a freelance collector with his three sons. In 1908, he was the first to find a mummified duck-billed *Edmontosaurus*.

Charles Sternberg

Sternberg's mummified
Edmontosaurus
ed-MON-tuh-SAWR-us

A Real Dinosaur Dig

Where do fossil hunters find dinosaur bones? How do they go about removing those bones from the earth? ICR's Daryl Robbins and Brian Thomas traveled to Montana in the summer of 2014 to find out.

Their destination was the Hell Creek Formation, a huge set of rock layers that sprawls across eastern Montana. Scientists have found some of the world's best-preserved dinosaur fossils in outcrops of this formation. Robbins and Thomas joined a group at a privately owned site just outside the city of Glendive for a three-day dig.

Badlands near Glendive, Montana

The Dig Landscape

The dig took place on an exposed part of a tiny hilltop. Earlier groups had removed about five feet of material to get down to the fossil zone. The dig area is surrounded by hills and valleys with sandstone cliffs and mudstone troughs. The sedimentary layers include plenty of clay deposits and some shale, plus coal seams here and there. Vegetation is sparse. To find out where to dig, fossil prospectors look for tiny dinosaur bone fragments lying on the ground, weathered and fragile. These fragments indicate that more fossils are buried nearby.

The Fossils They Found

Over three days, the diggers found an array of interesting fossils. The dinosaur fossils included rib bone fragments, a possible arm bone fragment, a small section of an ossified tendon, and a tail vertebra. But there were also a crocodile skull fragment, a turtle leg bone, a softshell turtle shell fragment, a fig, a seed pod, a shark tooth, a scale from a large gar fish, broken wood chunks (preserved only in shape with a thin iron-rich coating), and a horsetail rush stem segment. Of all these, only the dinosaurs have gone extinct.

Fig

The Digger's Tools

The dig tools were pretty simple. First, a broad-blade pickaxe removed fossil-poor sediment from an upper layer. Then, a flathead screwdriver scraped away the hard-packed sand of the fossil layer. When a fossil was encountered, a small, wooden-handled paintbrush carefully brushed away the surrounding sand. If the fossil had cracks, the dig supervisor brought a bottle of cyanoacrylate-based glue (basically, diluted superglue) to dribble into the crack and hold the fossil together. Shovels removed unwanted sand from the dig site, and some of that sand was sifted with screens to sort finer sediments into a wheelbarrow or bucket for closer inspection.

Crocodile skull fragment (left)

Horsetail rush stem (lower left), turtle bone (above), and seed pod (lower right)

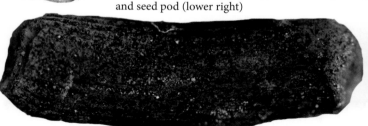

LIFE IN THE FIELD

Conducting a fossil dig presents the same challenges as other outdoor jobs. Those without sunscreen or proper clothing suffered sunburns. In the mornings, insect repellent was needed to protect against biting insects. In the afternoons, strong winds blew dust in the diggers' eyes and crumpled the sunshade umbrellas. These were small prices to pay for the experience of discovering the fossils. During the old days of the famous fossil wars, diggers worked in almost all conditions.

Dig site

MAKING A PLASTER CAST

Large fossil bone sections are cast in plaster to keep them from falling apart. First, material is removed from above and along the sides of a fossil. Then, tinfoil is pressed over it. Cloth strips are dipped into a mixture of water and plaster of Paris and laid over the tinfoil, making an upside-down bowl. Finally, the sediment beneath the fossil is carefully cut out, and the package is removed and turned over. The remaining sediment is brushed away, revealing what had been the bottom of the fossil.

THE CONDITION OF THE FOSSILS

The uncovered fossils were mostly small and fragmented. It looked as though the ancient water and swamp creatures were swept away and tumbled together until every bone was separated and broken into smaller bits. Some uncommonly forceful event spread this fractured mixture across a wide area. Perhaps during Noah's Flood, the material was mixed and spread out when the floodwaters receded off the continent's surface. Not all dinosaur fossils from the Hell Creek Formation are in as distressed a state, but most of the fossils are in pieces.

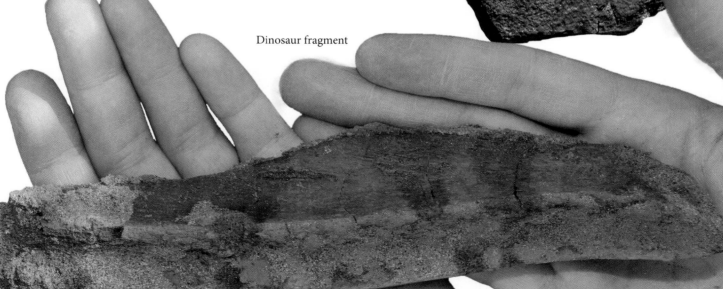

Turtle carapace

Dinosaur fragment

A Dinosaur Buried with a Fish

This *Sinosauropteryx* (SYN-uh-sawr-OP-ter-ix), a small, land-dwelling dinosaur, was found buried in a rock next to a modern-looking fish, which presumably could only live in water. The two animals were buried quickly before a larger animal could scavenge them and before bacteria could decompose their remains. Paleontologists often find dinosaur remains mixed with modern creatures like fish and mammals and preserved in sedimentary rock layers. Such rock layers could only form from a catastrophic watery event such as the great Flood of Noah's day, which quickly buried animals from different environments together and preserved them for us to study today.

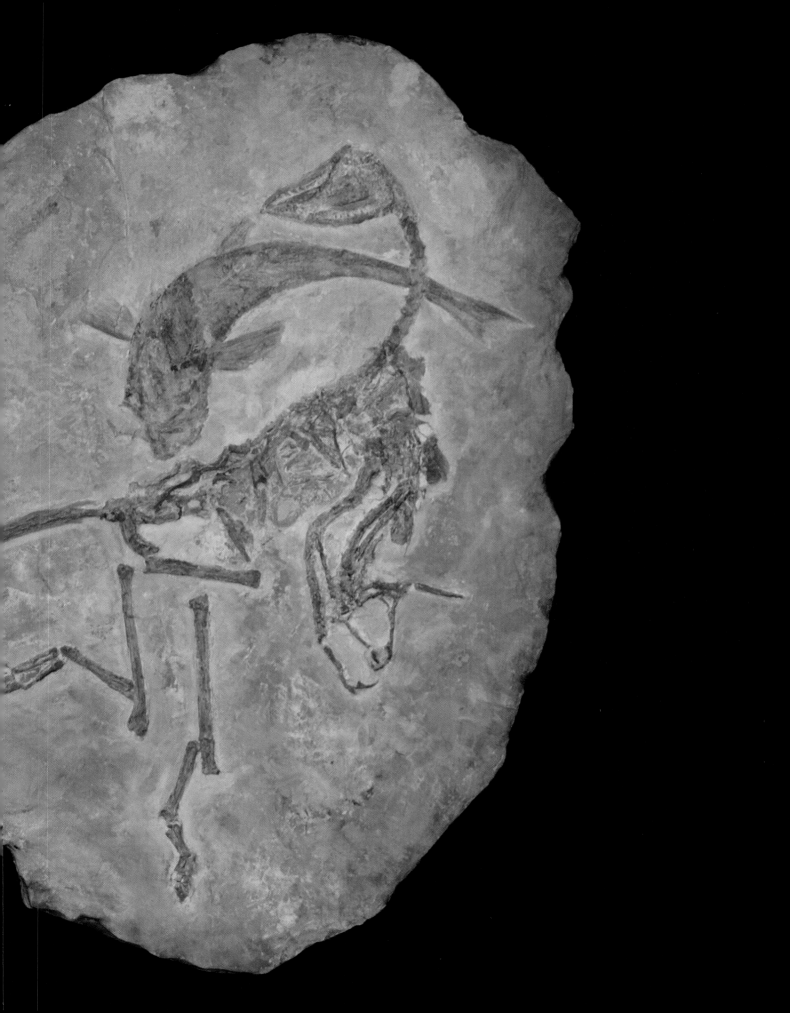

Early Expeditions in Africa and Asia

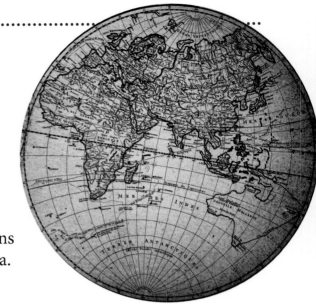

Dinosaur hunters digging in North America found many dinosaur fossils in rock formations such as the Morrison and Hell Creek Formations. However, bones of the great land reptiles were also discovered during expeditions in Africa and Asia in the early 1900s. Explorers uncovered new types of dinosaurs, but they also found remains from dinosaurs that had been discovered in North America.

Werner Janensch

THE GREAT EAST AFRICAN DINOSAUR EXPEDITION

Between 1909 and 1912, the Germans mounted what was probably the most spectacular dinosaur expedition of all time. Paleontologist Eberhard Fraas showed Wilhelm von Branca, the director of the Berlin Museum, some fossils collected in 1908 near the village of Tendaguru in what is now Tanzania. Branca immediately organized an expedition to collect more fossils, and he placed paleontologists Werner Janensch and Edward Hennig in charge. In all, about 250 tons of bones and rock were excavated from the site and had to be hand-carried on a four-day journey to the coast for shipment to Germany.

One of the most spectacular finds was a nearly complete *Brachiosaurus* that still resides as the showpiece of the Berlin Museum after surviving the bombings of World War II. This discovery demonstrated that some dinosaurs had greater distribution than previously thought. The first, partial skeleton of *Brachiosaurus* was unearthed in the western United States and described by American paleontologist Elmer Riggs in 1903. Janensch published a description of the German specimen in 1914.

Oddly, no one at the time offered an explanation for how the same dinosaurs could have co-existed on separate continents. However, the supercontinent that likely existed before the great Flood of Noah's day would have provided physical access to both areas. The Flood's water could have later deposited the remains of the dinosaurs on what are now separate continents.

Brachiosaurus
BRACK-ee-uh-SAWR-us

THE CENTRAL ASIATIC EXPEDITIONS

Five separate expeditions embarked into Central Asia to search for fossils between 1922 and 1930. Henry Fairfield Osborn, president of the American Museum of Natural History at the time, believed that Asia was the evolutionary origin site of many dominant land animals, including humans. Scientists had previously gathered extensive fossil collections in the Americas and in Europe, but information from Asia was lacking. So, Roy Chapman Andrews, a biologist and relatively new employee of the American Museum, proposed a venture to the Gobi Desert of Mongolia and organized the largest American expedition to ever leave the States. His crew was unique in that he brought along many scientific disciplines to supplement one another. Andrews also used cars and trucks for the expedition party and camel caravans to transport gasoline, supplies, and fossils. His team found a "gold mine" of dinosaurs and, most remarkably, the first recognized dinosaur eggs.

DID YOU KNOW?

Roy Chapman Andrews (1884-1960) is claimed to be the model for the movie character Indiana Jones. He wore a similar broad-brimmed hat, often sported a rifle, and had a zest for life and the dramatic. He made the cover of *Time* magazine for his discoveries in 1923.

Roy Chapman Andrews

In the Flaming Cliffs, 300 miles south of Urga, Mongolia, Andrews' team discovered clutches of dinosaur eggs, which they believed were laid by the new species they also discovered nearby—*Protoceratops*. After finding embryos in similar eggs years later, scientists now know the eggs were laid by a theropod called *Oviraptor*.

Fossilized dinosaur egg

Oviraptor
OH-vuh-RAP-ter

Protoceratops
pro-toe-SEH-ruh-tops

Finding Ages

Some people think we can learn the age of an object—like a dinosaur or a rock—by placing a sample of the object in a machine and running some laboratory tests. However, trying to date an object through these processes is far more complicated than that, and the tests are not entirely accurate. This is because dating processes begin with assumptions—for instance, that certain isotopes (variations of chemical elements) within an object decay or escape from the object into the atmosphere at a steady rate. Also, trying to measure the age of an object can sometimes yield mixed results. Determining the actual age of a rock or dinosaur bone requires the same thing that determines the age of a toaster oven or a person—a written or witnessed record of when it was manufactured or when he or she was born.

RADIOISOTOPE DATING AND BRACKETING

Scientists have ways to measure radioactive isotopes of uranium, thorium, rubidium, strontium, argon, and potassium in igneous rocks, like lava and ash flows. Problems arise when they try to use these measurements to determine a rock's age, a process called radioisotope dating, since doing so requires them to assume factors that may not have been observed. Lab tests have found that certain radioactive isotope decay rates fluctuate, so trying to determine a rock's age by that process is unreliable. Other radioisotope systems cannot be trusted because the initial amounts of decay product are unknown. Unlike igneous rocks, sedimentary rocks are usually mixtures of various weathered terrains and therefore give mixed ages if analyzed. Fossils, because they are found in sedimentary rocks, cannot normally be dated directly using radioactive isotopes, especially if they are thoroughly mineralized.

So, secular geologists estimate dates for most fossils by bracketing. To bracket a fossil, scientists need a layer of igneous rock, like a volcanic ash bed or a lava flow, above and below the layer containing the fossil. They estimate the age of the igneous rock with radioactive techniques that are assumed to be accurate. They then bracket the fossil's age between the two calculated dates. Usually, no ash layer or lava flow is near the fossils. This then requires correlating the rocks and fossils with rocks and fossils elsewhere that have ash layers and/or lava flows nearby. But since radioisotope dating is not a reliable method, neither is bracketing.

DID YOU KNOW?

Water will selectively dissolve many natural substances, including radioisotope decay products. All rocks and minerals below the water table are in constant contact with water, and dinosaur bones found in such rocks may return different radioactive isotope measurements than the same types of bones found in rocks that are not in contact with water.

Granite, like this piece, is a type of igneous rock. It is usually found in continental—rather than oceanic—plates.

A mass spectrometer is an instrument that scientists use to measure the masses and relative concentrations of atoms and molecules, such as isotopes in igneous rocks.

CARBON DATING

Carbon dating involves detecting how much carbon-14 (a radioactive isotope of the element carbon that decays into nitrogen-14) is left in an object. Repeated lab tests have shown that carbon-14 has a half-life of about 5,730 years, and any object older than 100,000 years should not have any carbon-14 left at all. But materials such as dinosaur bones and even diamonds have been shown to have measurable carbon-14 levels still in them. In short, they cannot possibly be older than 100,000 years, and they are obviously much younger since we can still measure carbon-14 in them.

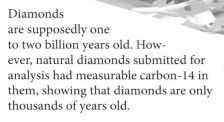

Diamonds are supposedly one to two billion years old. However, natural diamonds submitted for analysis had measurable carbon-14 in them, showing that diamonds are only thousands of years old.

Mummified human remains contain measurable amounts of carbon-14. However, just knowing the amount of carbon-14 in an object may not tell us exactly how old that object is. In the case of some mummies, we can determine their approximate ages based on historical records left behind in the form of engraved hieroglyphics on the tombs in which they are found.

HADROSAUR BONE TEST

This bone from a hadrosaur (duck-billed dinosaur) was found in a Hell Creek Formation outcrop in South Dakota and was labeled as 68 million years old. When sent in for carbon-dating tests, it still had measurable carbon-14 in it, and it returned with a result of 20,850 carbon years. While carbon years cannot be directly translated to calendar years without more unobservable assumptions, this measurement shows that this dinosaur bone—and the dinosaur it belonged to—is not nearly 68 million years old.

Samples from United States coal beds, which are supposedly 40 to 329 million years old, still contained measurable amounts of carbon-14, showing that they are not nearly as old as previously assumed.

Soft Fossil Discoveries

In evolution's story, dinosaurs lived and died out millions and millions of years ago. But did you know some dinosaur fossils still have partly decayed remains of their original body tissues? If these fossils are millions of years old, this biological material would be long gone! To understand why this is important, we need to understand something called uniformitarianism.

The biblical genealogies place the earth's age around 6,000 years old. But in the late 18th and into the 19th centuries, geologists began to develop a philosophy of uniformitarianism, in which Earth's processes were viewed as unchanging and progressing at very slow rates. In 1859, Charles Darwin published *On the Origin of Species*. Since his theory of natural selection cannot change one kind of organism into a different kind within a person's lifetime, Darwin had to include vast amounts of time for evolution to seem viable.

Uniformitarians ran with this idea, applying vast ages to everything—including fossils, rocks, and stars—thereby undermining Scripture. This was unscientific, however, because science is conducted based on observation by humans, and there are no human records of millions or billions of years. Without historical records, vast age estimates cannot be verified. Also, observable and testable discoveries in recent times, such as soft material in dinosaur fossils, show that these animals and the rocks containing them cannot possibly be older than thousands of years.

COLLAGEN

Dinosaur bone is made of a hard mineral called bioapatite and a softer protein called collagen, both produced by bone cells. Most fossilized bones have their soft parts replaced with inorganic minerals from groundwater. However, scientists have been able to find collagen, as well as blood vessels and cells, in dinosaur bones that are supposedly millions of years old. Chemical studies have shown that collagen cannot last longer than 900,000 years at normal Earth-surface temperatures before fully degrading, and yet researchers have found measurable collagen in dinosaur bones labeled as 180 million years old. Red blood cells and blood vessels would likely break down even quicker than collagen. This all shows that the dinosaurs these fossils belonged to were deposited no more (and likely far less) than 900,000 years ago, which is consistent with the Bible's historical record.

SOFT MARINE REPTILE FOSSILS

For decades, secular scientists have described original biochemicals like proteins not only in dinosaur fossils, but also in other fossil creatures. The mosasaur fossil shown here came from chalk rock in Kansas. Although this marine reptile was discovered in the 1960s, scientists did not publish a description of it until 2010. They found mosasaur skin scales covering the ancient carcass and two red patches inside the chest cavity—right where the heart and liver are situated in dolphins. The scientists' tests detected partly decayed blood protein hemoglobin only in the red patches. The science of decay shows that biochemicals like these cannot last for millions of years, but they can last thousands of years if kept cool, dry, and sterile.

SOFT DINOSAUR FOSSILS

Soft material was found in a broken *Tyrannosaurus rex* bone, and further study revealed that the material was original collagen and blood vessels still containing red blood cells. The discovery, made in the mid-2000s, met with resistance since these materials could not survive for 70 million years, the supposed age of the *T. rex* bone. Additional testing has proven that the soft tissue discovery was real. Other scientists have reported finding soft tissues in dinosaurs such as hadrosaurs, titanosaurs, psittacosaurs, ceratopsians, and others. Discoveries of preserved dinosaur soft tissue are no longer unusual.

DID YOU KNOW?

Scientists have even found dinosaur DNA. Tests show that DNA decays too fast to last millions of years. DNA kept at refrigerator temperatures would completely fall apart into tiny molecules of air and residue after about 350,000 years—far fewer than a million.

Animal	Evolutionary Supposed Age (millions of yrs)	Biochemical Found	Publish Date	Reference
T. rex	68	Collagen	Jun. 2007	Schweitzer, M. *Science*
Psittacosaurus	125	Collagen	Apr. 2008	Linghan-Soliar, T. *Proc. RSB*
Hadrosaur	80	Elastin	Jul. 2009	Schweitzer, M. *Science*
Mosasaur	65-68	Hemoglobin	Aug. 2010	Lindgren, J. *PLoS ONE*
Lizard	40	Keratin	Mar. 2011	Edwards, N. P. *Proc. RSB*
Mosasaur	70	Collagen	Apr. 2011	San Antonio, J. D. *PLoS ONE*
Squid	160	Eumelanin	May 2012	Glass, K. *PNAS*
Scorpion	310	Chitin + protein	Feb. 2011	Cody, G.D. *Geology*

This chart gives a brief list of some of the different kinds of biochemicals that have been found within a diverse group of fossilized creatures. Scientists continue to find original tissues in fossils that are supposedly too old to contain any organic remains at all.

Dinosaur Vegetation

Grasses and flowering plants, such as roses and sassafras, supposedly evolved millions of years after dinosaurs became extinct. However, paleontologists have uncovered specimens of "modern" trees and plants, including flowering plants, in rock layers above, below, and mixed in with dinosaur bones and other animals. And dinosaur coprolites (fossilized dung) have been found with grass in them. That means that these grasses, plants, and trees—many of which still exist today—lived at the same time as the dinosaurs. And that makes sense if all the plants and animals were created around the same time, just as the book of Genesis records.

Oak tree

Rice

Sassafras

Roses

Palms

Magnolia

Cycad

Ferns

Sequoia trees

Animals Mixed with Dinosaurs

According to evolution, when dinosaurs were alive there weren't many non-reptile land animals around, and the few that existed were "primitive." But many modern-looking land creatures, including birds and insects, have been found in the same fossil layers as dinosaurs and even mixed with dinosaurs themselves. In fact, every major group of vertebrates has been found in dinosaur rocks. If evolution is true, then dinosaur fossils should primarily be found by themselves. But if the Bible is true that all animals and plants had been created by the end of the sixth day, then dinosaur remains should be found mixed with many kinds of creatures like these—which they are!

Parrot

Turtle

Dragonfly

Tasmanian devil

Squirrel

Crocodile

Albatross

Coelacanth

Duck

Spider

LIVING FOSSILS

Sometimes living animals or plants are found that were thought to have been extinct for millions of years. These are called living fossils. Perhaps the most famous example is the coelacanth fish, which evolutionists originally considered an evolutionary "missing link" between fish and amphibians. It was supposed to have died out around 70 million years ago (since its fossils don't appear in upper strata), yet a live one was found in 1938 off the coast of Africa. If evolution is true, where was the coelacanth for over 70 million years, and why is it virtually unchanged? Lots of other living fossils—from magnolia flowers to gar fish, and from single-cell algal filaments to lobsters—have been found. The simplest explanation for why they haven't changed is that they did not evolve but were instead all created recently.

Cockroach

Frog

Gar

Attack and Defense Measures

Predatory dinosaurs are portrayed in movies as hunting in coordinated attacks, but most of what's in the movies is speculation. The common consensus seems to be that smaller predators hunted in packs, similar to wolves, while the larger *T. rex*-size predators hunted alone or in small groups like lions. These notions are based mostly on modern mammals and on some fossil evidence. Unfortunately, there is a limit to deriving behavior from fossils alone. The best way to be sure how animals behave is to observe them, and sadly, there are no more dinosaurs around for us to do that.

FIGHTING

Like other animals, dinosaurs most likely fought for food, territory, and to protect their offspring. Sauropods could have used their long necks and tails to defend against attackers, but their immense size alone could have been a deterrent against attacks. *Ankylosaurus* had a club-like tail with which it could fight, and *Stegosaurus* had a formidable tail covered in spikes. And the ceratopsian dinosaurs had horns on their heads and probably used them to charge at other animals, similar to cattle and bighorn sheep.

LIVING OR FLEEING IN PACKS?

Paleontologists have found footprints and fossils of plant-eating dinosaurs grouped together. This was probably an effective deterrent against attacks from predators, especially for young dinosaurs that did not yet have protective clubs, spikes, or horns, or the tough skin and large size of some adult dinosaurs.

Tyrannosaurus and *Spinosaurus*
tye-RAN-uh-SAWR-us and SPY-no-SAWR-us

Groups of meat-eating dinosaurs have also been found together. From the small *Coelophysis* to the larger *Allosaurus*, theropods have been found in groups of over 40, and the famous *T. rex* "Sue"—featured at the Field Museum of Natural History in Chicago—was excavated out of rock containing the fragments of three other *T. rex* individuals. Paleontologists also have footprint evidence that showed that theropods traveled together, although not usually in large herds.

Saurolophus herd
sawr-OL-oh-fus

Finding fossils and footprints of different dinosaurs grouped together might show that the animals involved were fleeing together. When water levels rose during the great Flood, these dinosaurs could have been trying to escape. Tracks like these were made in mud, which hardened later and preserved them, so we know there was water at the time. Theropod tooth marks occur in hadrosaur bones, but the tracks of these two dinosaur types—obviously made at the same time—do not show pursuit. Maybe they were too exhausted after surviving the first part of the Flood.

Ankylosaurus
ang-KYE-luh-SAWR-us

Stegosaurus
STEG-uh-SAWR-us

VELOCIRAPTOR VS. PROTOCERATOPS

One of the most spectacular fossils ever found is from Mongolia and shows a *Velociraptor* and *Protoceratops* locked in a death struggle. While many textbooks say that fossils form when a creature dies and is slowly covered by sediment over time, this fossil clearly shows that these two dinosaurs were alive when they were suddenly buried by enough sediment and water to preserve their fight. One of the many muddy pulses from the Flood of Noah's day would have been the type of event to do just this.

Apatosaurus
uh-PAT-uh-SAWR-us

Did Dinosaurs Evolve into Birds?

Most museums and textbooks have dinosaur displays or pictures showing dinosaurs with colorful feathers. These reflect the popular belief that an unidentified theropod dinosaur evolved into the first bird, which then evolved into the other bird kinds. But not every evolutionary scientist agrees with this. Some evolutionary researchers don't believe that dinosaurs had feathers, and others disagree over which kind of dinosaur—if any—might have evolved into birds while all the other dinosaur kinds went extinct.

The Bible clearly teaches that God made each creature to reproduce after its own kind. Dogs can only make dogs, cats can only make cats, and ducks can only make ducks. Despite evolutionary displays that emphasize the similarities between dinosaurs and birds, these two animal types were actually very different. And no process of biology or nature has so far demonstrated an ability to change a dinosaur body into a bird body. It looks like each dinosaur kind and each bird kind was created, just like the Bible has said all along.

Sinosauropteryx
SY-no-sawr-OP-ter-ix

DINO-FEATHERS?

Dinosaur fossils have been found with fibers that some scientists thought were "proto-feathers," the beginnings of feather evolution. However, the fibers didn't have the same structure as feathers, so they were later called filaments. What are they? Scientists tested animal skin that was decaying in water. After several days, the skin turned into stringy protein fibers that looked virtually identical to fossil dinosaur-skin "filaments." So, not only do the fossil fibers *not* look like feathers, they *do* look like partly decayed skin.

DID YOU KNOW?

Sometimes a new fossil is described as a "feathered dinosaur" only to be reclassified later as an extinct bird. Other supposed feathered dinosaurs—like *Sinosauropteryx*—were clearly reptiles and not birds at all.

NO FOLLICLES

If dinosaurs evolved into birds, then at some point they had to begin growing feathers. But feathers are produced by very specialized tissues inside large cavities called follicles, and dinosaur skin fossils show smooth, scaly reptile skin with no follicles. Their "scales" were actually thickened bumps of skin. If dinosaurs evolved feathers, how did they grow and how were they attached?

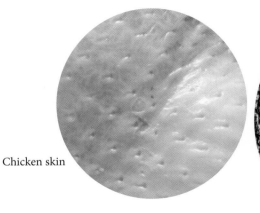

Chicken skin

Hadrosaurus skin
HAD-roh-SAWR-us

BIRDS AND DINOSAURS MIXED TOGETHER

Birds supposedly evolved from dinosaurs, but bird fossils have been found with dinosaurs. Ducks, loons, albatross, other water birds, and parrots have been discovered, as well as extinct bird kinds including some with clawed wings. If evolution is true, we should find dinosaurs in lower rock layers, part-dinosaur/part-bird animals in middle layers, and birds in upper layers. Instead, dinosaurs and birds are all mixed together.

BIRD FOSSILS FOUND BEFORE DINOSAURS

Some evolutionary researchers have reported the discovery of bird tracks in rock layers that were located below, and thus deposited before, layers containing dinosaurs. How could they have evolved from dinosaurs that didn't even exist yet?

Bird fossil

DID YOU KNOW?

Many of the rock layers that contain "fibered" dinosaur fossils also have fully formed birds. Because they lived and died at the same time, dinosaurs and birds do not show an ancestor-descendant relationship.

IT'S ALL IN THE HIPS

In order for a theropod dinosaur to evolve into a bird, it would have to reorganize almost every bone in its skeleton, including the hips. Dinosaurs walked like people, with the upper legs moving at the hip joint, but birds walk at their knees. Their upper legs stay stiffened into a position that helps support their unique breathing system and aerodynamic shape. At some point in its journey, the evolving dinosaur would have lost its ability to walk!

DISTINCTIVE LUNG SYSTEMS

Like other reptiles, most dinosaurs likely breathed with bellows-type lungs. Air filled the lung sacs and then emptied out the way it had come in. But birds use an efficient flow-through lung in which air travels in one end and out the other. At some point, an evolving transitional creature would have been left without its reptile lungs but also without its new bird lungs. Unable to breathe, its evolution would have come to a screeching halt.

Bird hip

Theropod hip

DINO/BIRD FAKE

In 1999, the National Geographic Society announced the discovery of a half-bird/half-dinosaur fossil they called *Archaeoraptor*. The Society quickly announced the so-called "feathered" dinosaur before scientists carefully reviewed the specimen, which turned out to be a complete fake.

Archaeoraptor
ARK-ee-oh-RAP-ter

Visiting a Museum

If you want to learn about dinosaurs and fossils, there's no substitute for seeing them up close. But this often means going to secular museums, which usually describe dinosaurs within a strictly evolutionary context. For example, a display might say that dinosaurs evolved into birds, but it won't mention or show the bird fossils that paleontologists have found buried alongside dinosaurs—evidence that directly contradicts the dinosaur-to-bird story.

Despite the evolutionary descriptions, with the right preparation such a visit can have big benefits. Armed with firsthand knowledge, a visitor becomes better equipped to discern what the real dinosaur story is.

Also, dealing with the evolutionary falsehoods in such places can help prepare younger students for the exposure to evolution they will encounter in school and in the media. They will come to realize that scientific evidence, correctly understood, supports the Bible. Here are some suggestions for getting the most out of a visit to a secular dinosaur museum.

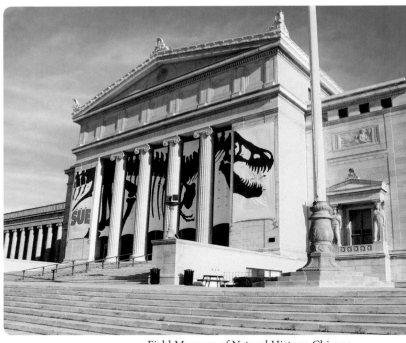

Field Museum of Natural History, Chicago

THE MEANING OF "NATURAL HISTORY"

Many dinosaur museums have the words "natural history" in their names. What does that mean? Where do we typically find legitimate, trustworthy sources of information about the past? The best sources of history are written by the people who experienced certain events. In contrast, scientific evidence does not speak for itself. Instead, we fit it into a story we already have in mind. Understand that the evidence you will see in a secular dinosaur museum will be presented according to the evolutionary story. In spite of what evolutionists say, nature's processes do not reveal history, but the written eyewitness accounts in the Bible do.

MILLIONS OF YEARS

Secular museums usually describe Earth's history in terms of millions or even billions of years. People who believe the biblical timeline of just thousands of years should equip themselves with evidence that refutes old-earth ideas. For instance, secular scientists claim that radioisotope dating methods prove long ages for rocks and fossils. If this were true, those methods should supply accurate ages for rocks of known age—but they don't. In 1996, ICR geologists submitted a 10-year-old rock to radioisotope analyses that found "ages" ranging from 60,000 to almost three million years! There are many Earth "clocks" that indicate a young age, such as the amount of salt in the ocean and the strength of Earth's magnetic field. The millions of years assigned to rocks and fossils do not come from good science but from belief-based traditions. Observe how many times the museum's displays cite "millions of years" without providing any evidence to support this.

TRANSITIONAL FORMS?

The descriptions in secular dinosaur museums usually reflect the evolutionary claim that genetic mistakes over eons turned some unknown ancient reptile into all the dinosaur kinds, and later into birds. If this story is true, what would the fossil evidence show? Instead of transitional features like half a bird beak or a half-leg/half-fin, animals show complete and expert design the first time they appear in the fossil record. Search the museum specimens to see if you can find the partly formed skeletal features that evolution predicts. Compare your findings to the number of properly proportioned, well-fitted body parts that don't fit the evolutionary story.

Lambeosaur

DINOSAUR DESIGN

Rather than showing transitional features or other marks of evolution, dinosaur fossils reveal marvelous engineering in how they're put together. For example, sauropod necks had special, lightweight vertebrae that allowed them to raise their heads high enough to eat from the trees that produced their food. And their hips were designed like arches to bear the weight of their enormous bodies. As you go through the museum, see what other design features you can find in dinosaurs.

"HOW DO THEY KNOW THAT?"

Visiting a secular dinosaur museum provides a good opportunity to exercise critical thinking. Select an evolutionary statement from any museum description and ask, "How do they know that?" Many dinosaur museums have docents, volunteers who answer questions. You could ask them this one. It might even turn into a ministry opportunity.

LIVING FOSSILS

Living fossils are scattered throughout most dinosaur fossil museums. A living fossil—such as the coelacanth—is a plant or animal that is found living today virtually unchanged even though it was thought to have been extinct for millions of years. As you explore the museum, see how many living fossils you can find. Each time you see a fossil creature that looks like a modern living creature, you see evidence against evolution. After supposedly millions of years of mutations and selection, why didn't evolution make any significant changes? Maybe it's because evolution didn't happen.

Crocodile

Dinosaur Kinds

Dinosaur Varieties

Our modern classification system lists over 1,000 species of dinosaurs, and about 20 to 30 new species are named each year. But the same dinosaur species have often been named more than once (i.e., *Brontosaurus* and *Apatosaurus*). This disturbing trend started back in the latter half of the 19th century with paleontologists Othniel Charles Marsh and Edward Drinker Cope competing to name the most dinosaurs. Marsh and Cope named many species based on just a few bones and rarely published drawings for comparison.

Edward Drinker Cope

MARSH AND COPE'S BONE WARS

Between 1870 and 1899, Marsh named 80 different dinosaur species, but only 29% were subsequently found to be new or distinct. The other 71% he named were synonyms or repeats that he or someone else had already named. He eventually ended up with only 23 distinct species to his credit. Cope had a success rate of only 14% but managed to name nine new species that withstood later review.

Othniel Charles Marsh

British paleontologist Michael Benton estimates that the overall success rate in naming a new dinosaur species has been about 50%. American paleontologist John R. Horner has stated that as many as 40% of known dinosaur species may be repeats of the same species but in different stages of growth and development. A lot of this is due to the incomplete nature of most dinosaur discoveries.

THE SAME DINOSAUR?

Paleontologists John Ostrom and Peter Wellnhofer proposed that the 16 named species of the genus *Triceratops* (a ceratopsian) could be reduced to just a single species. They believed that all variations observed within the 16 species are no different from the observed variations seen in modern bovids (i.e., cattle). There is even convincing evidence that *Triceratops* and *Torosaurus* may be the same genus. After studying over 50 specimens, some scientists determined that *Triceratops* is merely an advanced juvenile version of *Torosaurus*, possibly leaving us without the genus *Triceratops* altogether.

Triceratops
try-SEH-ruh-tops

DINOSAUR CLASSIFICATION

The question of which modern species belong within the same kind is an exciting area of research. Creation biologists are actively working out the limits of variation within a kind to better understand where it falls in our modern taxonomic system. This table lists the accepted dinosaur groupings. There are five accepted suborders, 13 infraorders, and 60 families of dinosaurs, and a family may approximate a kind.

KINDS VS. SPECIES

There are a lot fewer kinds of dinosaurs than those that are named as species. The Bible teaches that during the creation week God made discrete kinds of organisms that are reproductively isolated from one another. Amazingly, God placed in each kind the ability to diversify into many breeds or even species that nonetheless remain the same basic kind. For example, dogs have diversified into retrievers, beagle, dachshunds, and so on, but they remain dogs. There is no biblical reason to assume a kind is the same as a species or that it lines up with any particular level of our modern taxonomic system.

DINOSAURIA

SAURISCHIA

THEROPODA
- HERRERASAURIA
- CERATOSAURIA
- CARNOSAURIA
- COELUROSAURIA
- THERIZINOSAURIDAE

SAUROPODOMORPHA
- SAUROPODA
- PROSAUROPODA

ORNITHISCHIA

ORNITHOPODA
- FABROSAURIDAE
- ORNITHOPODS

MARGINOCEPHALIA
- PACHYCEPHALOSAURIA
- CERATOPSIA

THYREOPHORA
- STEGOSAURIA
- ANKYLOSAURIA

Golden Retriever

Dachshund

Beagle

The definition of a species is difficult to quantify. It becomes even more difficult with extinct species since we do not get to observe their behavior. Biologist Ernst Mayr defined the term species as "groups of actually or potentially interbreeding natural populations, which are reproductively isolated from other groups." Unfortunately, paleontologists cannot observe the reproductive habits of dinosaurs to sort out species, and any small variation is usually called a new species.

Suborder Theropoda: The Meat-Eaters and More

The name theropod means "beast foot," and these dinosaurs had larger eyes and bigger brains than most others. They walked on two feet, had an extra hole (fenestra) in the skull to reduce weight, and had a jointed skull for flexibility in biting and chewing. Many of the theropod bones were hollow, and the head was attached to the neck by a very mobile joint. Theropods possessed a lizard-hipped pelvis, and they are the rarest of the dinosaur finds—making up less than 5% of discoveries. Most theropods fall into two groups: 1) ceratosaurs and 2) the Tetanurae.

T. rex

The ceratosaurs had many fused leg bones, allowing them to run faster. They commonly had horns or a crest along the top of the skull, leading to the name ceratosaur, "horned lizard." Included in this group are the dinosaurs *Coelophysis* and *Dilophosaurus*, and possibly the Herrerasauria.

The coelurosaurs ("hollow-tail lizards") further divided into at least three families: the tyrannosaurs, the ornithomimosaurs, and the dromaeosaurs. The dromaeosaurs include raptors like *Velociraptor* and *Deinonychus*. Some also lump the Therizinosauridae into this group, but the incomplete nature of most of these fossils makes classification difficult.

The Tetanurae ("fused-tail lizards") are further divided into two infraorders: 1) carnosaurs and 2) coelurosaurs. Tetanurae had a second opening in the skull, making them lighter in weight, and a differently designed hind leg to allow even faster movement. One family of carnosaurs ("meat lizards") is Allosauridae and includes *Allosaurus, Megalosaurus,* and *Spinosaurus.*

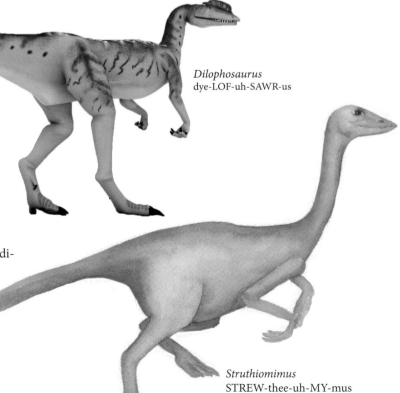

Dilophosaurus, a ceratosaur, appeared in the 1993 movie *Jurassic Park.* In the film, it spat some sort of toxin and had a neck flap that extended when agitated, but we cannot tell from the actual fossil evidence that these attributes were real. We do know from fossils, however, that it had two thin crests that ran the length of the skull.

Dilophosaurus
dye-LOF-uh-SAWR-us

Ornithomimosaurs were the "bird-mimic lizards." These dinosaurs looked like ostriches with long, bony tails. They apparently could run fast, since they were designed with long shin bones. They had a rather small skull and no teeth. These dinosaurs were likely plant-eaters, since gastroliths (stomach stones) have been found associated with some specimens.

Struthiomimus
STREW-thee-uh-MY-mus

Giganotosaurus
GIG-uh-NOTE-uh-SAWR-us

Giganotosaurus, found in Argentina in the mid-1990s, is one of the largest meat-eating dinosaurs discovered so far. It was about 43 feet long from its snout to the tip of its tail, and its teeth were smaller and thinner than *T. rex* teeth.

Spinosaurus
SPY-nuh-SAWR-us

Paleontologists discovered specimens of *Spinosaurus* in Africa that were up to 50 feet long. They had a large bony sail on their backs up to seven feet tall, although the exact purpose of this spine is unclear. The latest research indicates that spinosaurs spent a considerable part of their lives in water, possibly eating fish and other aquatic prey.

Researchers have found many specimens of *Allosaurus* throughout the American West, making it one of the more common theropods. A specimen called "Big Al" is one of the most complete dinosaurs ever found. It was discovered in the Bighorn Basin of northwestern Wyoming and resides in the University of Wyoming's Geology Museum. These dinosaur fossils are commonly found with the large sauropods (long-necks).

Allosaurus
AL-oh-SAWR-us

Tyrannosaurus rex: The Tyrant Lizard

Tyrannosaurus rex is likely the most famous predatory dinosaur of all. *Tyrannosaurus* means "tyrant lizard" in Greek, and *rex* means "king" in Latin. A 5.5-ton adult *T. rex*, if it were endothermic (warm-blooded), would have had to eat the equivalent of an adult hadrosaur (duck-billed dinosaur) each week to supply its hunger needs. If it were ectothermic (cold-blooded), it would have required a lot less—about a fifth or a tenth as much food, depending on its activity levels. Tooth marks on other dinosaurs match the dental patterns of the *T. rex*—even on another *T. rex* toe bone, suggesting that these dinosaurs were also cannibals. This not surprising, since most scientists think that they sometimes scavenged for food.

BIG BRAIN

Movies, comics, and other popular depictions like to portray dinosaur brains—especially of *T. rex*—as quite small. This fits the evolutionary theory that dinosaurs evolved into birds, and while bird-brained dinosaurs can be entertaining, this idea is not supported by the scientific evidence. Bird brains are not only smaller but also shaped very differently, and scans of *T. rex* skulls have shown that their brains were shaped and sized more like reptiles. All the available data also indicate that their intelligence, thought processing, and senses were probably similar to alligators. The *T. rex* brain cavity was also shaped to accommodate a large olfactory lobe, which would allow the dinosaur to have a great sense of smell.

Tyrannosaurus rex
tye-RAN-uh-SAWR-us rex

Big Bite

Studies of bite mechanics provided more data to support the notion that the *T. rex* was truly the "king of dinosaurs." Scientists in England used dynamic musculoskeletal models to simulate the bite strength of a *T. rex*. They found that it had a biting force of nearly double that of an equivalent-size alligator, with forces of 35,000–57,000 Newtons—about the same force generated by a medium-size elephant sitting on a person.

Growth Spurt

Tyrannosaurs grew slower than most dinosaurs, having a growth spurt in their teenage years as opposed to most dinosaurs, which grew faster much earlier in life. Some scientists believe the younger *T. rex* may actually have been able to run, but as it got larger it was forced to slow down due to its increased mass.

"Sue"

The most famous *Tyrannosaurus rex* fossil ever found is nicknamed "Sue" after the paleontologist, Sue Hendrickson, who discovered it in 1990 in South Dakota. Sue is over 40 feet long and stands about 14 feet tall, but what is remarkable is that over 90% of the skeleton is original. Most fossil finds are in fragments and finding a complete skeleton is rare, which is why Sue is so important. Along with Sue, researchers found the bones of three other partial *T. rex* skeletons.

Sue also made headlines when the federal government confiscated the entire skeleton, since it was found on Native American reservation grounds. The skeleton was locked away for three years during a court battle over ownership, which finally ended with an auction by Sotheby's. The Field Museum of Natural History in Chicago, along with help from Disney and McDonald's, won the auction with a bid of $8.4 million. Most of the money went to the owner of the land, and the rest went to the auction house. Sue Hendrickson, who made the discovery, received nothing but legal bills.

"Sue" the *T. rex*

Vegetarian Theropods?

Theropods are typically considered the meat-eaters of the dinosaur world since most have sharp serrated teeth similar in design to other carnivorous animals. But some theropods had leaf-shape teeth like herbivore dinosaurs, and others had no teeth at all. So, it is possible that some of these dinosaurs were omnivores or just herbivores. Paleontologists have even found fossils of certain dinosaurs with rocks in their stomachs called gastroliths. These probably helped with grinding up vegetation so that the dinosaurs could digest it.

Egg Thieves?

Paleontologists used to think that *Oviraptor* was an "egg thief" dinosaur because *Oviraptor* skeletons were found in the 1920s in Mongolia near what were once thought to be *Protoceratops* eggs. The formal name of *Oviraptor philoceratops* translates as "egg thief that loves ceratopsians." However, paleontologists discovered in the 1990s that *Oviraptor* was not the egg-eating animal it was portrayed to be. It was the mother of the eggs it was lying near, and an embryotic *Oviraptor* found in one of the eggs proved the match.

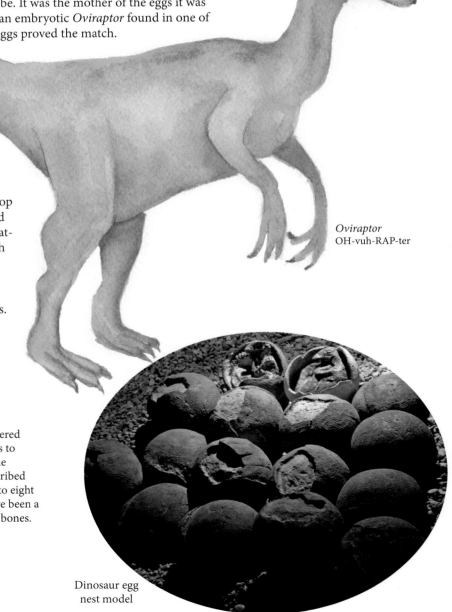

Oviraptor
OH-vuh-RAP-ter

Researchers found another adult *Oviraptor* buried and fossilized on top of another egg nest. Evolutionary scientists think that the "mother" dinosaur was incubating the eggs, but it is more likely that the dinosaur was merely caught in the act of laying the eggs and became trapped atop the nest as the waters and sediment of Noah's Flood engulfed them. *Oviraptor* is now thought to have eaten plants or possibly clams with its toothless mouth and "beak." One *Oviraptor* had a small lizard fossil in its stomach region, and most paleontologists assumed these dinosaurs were herbivores that may have supplemented their diets with smaller animals.

Discovery

American paleontologist Roy Chapman Andrews discovered *Oviraptor* on one of the early Central Asiatic Expeditions to Mongolia in the 1920s, and Henry Fairfield Osborn of the American Museum of Natural History in New York described and named it in 1924. An adult *Oviraptor* was about six to eight feet long and weighed about 55 to 75 pounds. It may have been a swift runner because it had long hind legs and long shin bones. Some researchers estimated its top speed at 40 mph.

Dinosaur egg
nest model

THERIZINOSAURUS

Most paleontologists now place therizinosaurs in the theropod suborder, but it was put in other groups in the past. *Therizinosaurus*—meaning "scythe reptile"—was named by Russian paleontologist Evgeny A. Maleev in 1954 after he discovered it in Mongolia in 1948. It had enormous three-foot-long claws on the forelimbs, which some scientists speculate were used to tear open termite or ant nests. Most paleontologists, however, assume *Therizinosaurus* was an herbivore based on its teeth. These dinosaurs were about 23 feet long, 10 feet tall, and are estimated to have weighed around three tons.

Therizinosaurus
THAIR-uh-ZEEN-uh-SAWR-us

STRUTHIOMIMUS

This dinosaur was first called *Ornithomimus* by dinosaur hunter Othniel Charles Marsh in 1892, but Henry Fairfield Osborn changed the name to *Struthiomimus*—meaning "ostrich mimic"—in 1917 after acquiring new specimens from Alberta. This dinosaur was about 13 feet long and weighed about 310 pounds. They had long necks and small skulls with large eyes and toothless beaks covered with keratin—the protein in fingernails and lizard scales. These dinosaurs also had long and slender forelimbs with large claws.

Struthiomimus
STROOTH-ee-uh-MY-mus

GALLIMIMUS

Gallimimus was another ornithomimosaurid found in Mongolia. It was similar to (and likely the same kind of dinosaur) as *Struthiomimus*. *Gallimimus* may have been some of the fastest-moving dinosaurs because they had long metatarsal bones tightly bound together in their feet. They also had long shin bones that could have allowed them to run up to 50 mph.

Gallimimus
GAL-uh-MY-mus

Velociraptor: The Little Threat

The movie *Jurassic Park* popularized the *Velociraptor* as a fast and ferocious creature that could chase people into small rooms and even
open doors. However, Hollywood took a few creative liberties—particularly in
the *Velociraptor* itself. The creature depicted in the movie was actually *Deinonychus*,
a dinosaur found in North America. *Velociraptor*, discovered in Mongolia, was much
smaller, likely much less intelligent, and nowhere near as vicious.

Velociraptor was about six feet long from nose to tail, but its body was only about the size of a
large turkey and weighed about 35 pounds. *Deinonychus*, by contrast, was about 10 to 11 feet
long and weighed about 150 pounds. However, biomechanical estimates have *Velociraptor*
running at top speeds of around 24 mph, which is faster than most humans.

Both *Velociraptor* and *Deinonychus* belonged to the group of theropods known as dromaeosaurs. And although their brain-to-body ratio was one of the largest of all dinosaurs, their
brains were still less than an equally-sized mammal, like a dog. That means *Velociraptor*
probably could not open doors on purpose or learn new behavior easily. Its brain was like all
theropod dinosaurs, closer in shape to that of a modern alligator, with a small brain section
for processing information and a large section for sensory perception.

Deinonychus
dye-NON-uh-kus

Deinonychus was the dinosaur in *Jurassic
Park* that was incorrectly called *Velociraptor*.
It was larger, but based on studying its brain
cavity, it was likely not intelligent enough to
learn to open doors.

Velociraptor
vuh-LOS-uh-RAPT-or

Velociraptor was about
the size of a large turkey.

Velociraptor

Turkey

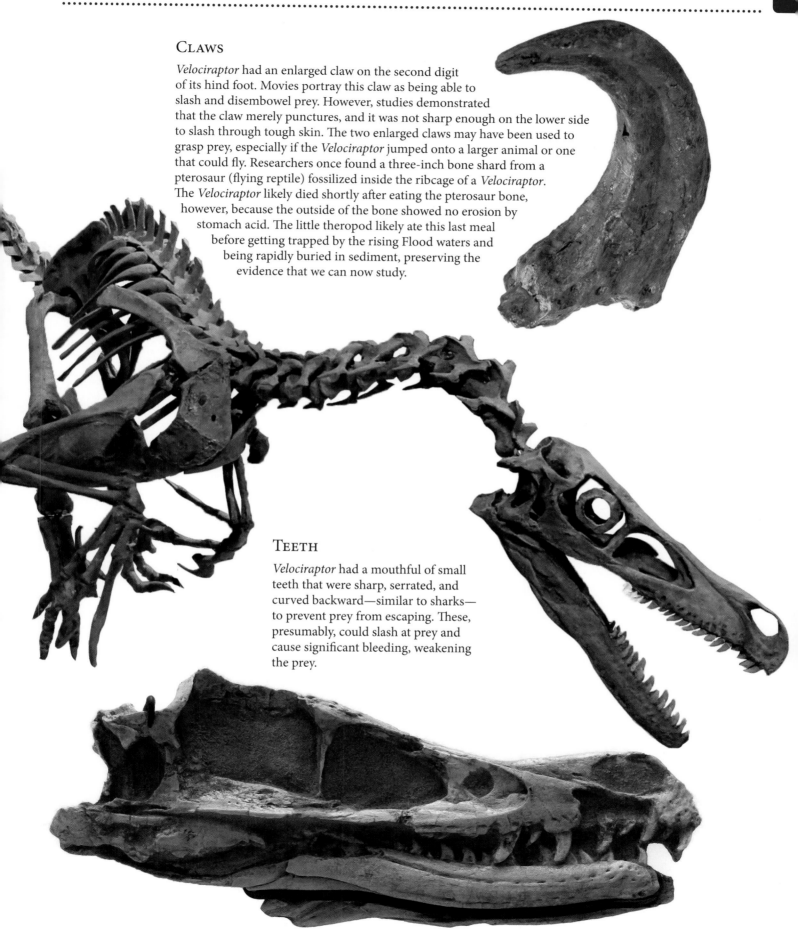

Claws

Velociraptor had an enlarged claw on the second digit of its hind foot. Movies portray this claw as being able to slash and disembowel prey. However, studies demonstrated that the claw merely punctures, and it was not sharp enough on the lower side to slash through tough skin. The two enlarged claws may have been used to grasp prey, especially if the *Velociraptor* jumped onto a larger animal or one that could fly. Researchers once found a three-inch bone shard from a pterosaur (flying reptile) fossilized inside the ribcage of a *Velociraptor*. The *Velociraptor* likely died shortly after eating the pterosaur bone, however, because the outside of the bone showed no erosion by stomach acid. The little theropod likely ate this last meal before getting trapped by the rising Flood waters and being rapidly buried in sediment, preserving the evidence that we can now study.

Teeth

Velociraptor had a mouthful of small teeth that were sharp, serrated, and curved backward—similar to sharks—to prevent prey from escaping. These, presumably, could slash at prey and cause significant bleeding, weakening the prey.

Allosaurus: The Land Shark

*A*llosaurus was one of the more common theropod dinosaurs whose fossils have been found throughout the American West in locations across Wyoming, Utah, Colorado, Montana, and New Mexico. The name *Allosaurus* means "different reptile," but this dinosaur was not always known by this name. In 1870, paleontologist Joseph Leidy named a new partial dinosaur skeleton *Antrodemus*, which means "body cavity." A different specimen of this same dinosaur found near Cañon City, Colorado, was later called *Allosaurus* by paleontologist Othniel Charles Marsh in 1877. It was not until the mid-20th century that the names were combined. Most scientists place *Allosaurus* in the category Tetanurae ("fused tails") and in the infraorder carnosaur ("meat reptile").

The adult *Allosaurus* could grow to a length of about 30 feet, but some paleontologists have found partial specimens that may have approached 40 feet in length. *Allosaurus* may have weighed between 1.5 to 2.5 tons and, compared to *Tyrannosaurus rex,* had rather small teeth for its size. The teeth only stuck up about two inches above the jawline but were thinner and very sharp, similar in shape to the tip of a sabre. These teeth may have cut prey like shark teeth, prompting some to call *Allosaurus* the land shark.

At least 44 adult specimens of *Allosaurus* were found buried together in one spot in central Utah. Known as the Cleveland-Lloyd Dinosaur Quarry, this site has been under excavation since the 1920s, but it was not until the 1960s that researchers extracted thousands of *Allosaurus* bones there. The quarry was created when a massive sediment flow mixed and tore apart the bodies and bones of the 44 allosaurs and gathered them into one condensed deposit during the great Flood of Noah's day.

The Cleveland-Lloyd Dinosaur Quarry is located in central Utah. Over 15,000 dinosaur bones have been uncovered at this location so far, and many more wait to be discovered.

Other than finding multiple specimens buried together by transport, like at the Cleveland-Lloyd Dinosaur Quarry in Utah, there is little evidence to suggest that *Allosaurus* was a pack hunter. Likewise, there is also little fossil evidence to support *Allosaurus* as a solitary hunter. Without living allosaurs to observe, we simply do not know how they hunted.

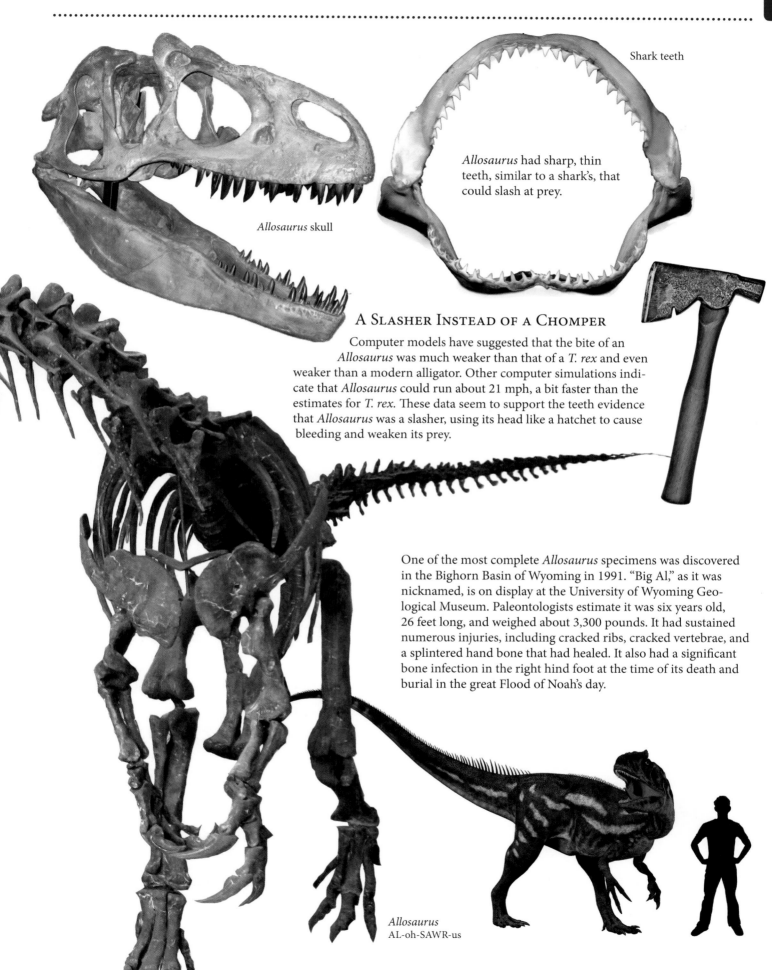

Shark teeth

Allosaurus skull

Allosaurus had sharp, thin teeth, similar to a shark's, that could slash at prey.

A Slasher Instead of a Chomper

Computer models have suggested that the bite of an *Allosaurus* was much weaker than that of a *T. rex* and even weaker than a modern alligator. Other computer simulations indicate that *Allosaurus* could run about 21 mph, a bit faster than the estimates for *T. rex*. These data seem to support the teeth evidence that *Allosaurus* was a slasher, using its head like a hatchet to cause bleeding and weaken its prey.

One of the most complete *Allosaurus* specimens was discovered in the Bighorn Basin of Wyoming in 1991. "Big Al," as it was nicknamed, is on display at the University of Wyoming Geological Museum. Paleontologists estimate it was six years old, 26 feet long, and weighed about 3,300 pounds. It had sustained numerous injuries, including cracked ribs, cracked vertebrae, and a splintered hand bone that had healed. It also had a significant bone infection in the right hind foot at the time of its death and burial in the great Flood of Noah's day.

Allosaurus
AL-oh-SAWR-us

Dilophosaurus: The Spitting Dinosaur?

In the movie *Jurassic Park*, *Dilophosaurus* is shown spitting some sort of poison on its prey before devouring it. But is there any scientific basis for this behavior in dinosaurs? The short answer is "no."

Although many dinosaur specimens have been found, including fossil bones and soft tissues such as proteins, collagen, bone cells, and red blood cells, researchers have not yet uncovered evidence of a spitting dinosaur. However, there are multiple examples of living reptiles and mammals that spit or spray some sort of toxic venom or foul-smelling liquid. And in Job 41:19-21, God describes the swimming creature called leviathan (possibly a type of mosasaur) as being able to spit "sparks of fire." So, it is possible that some dinosaurs like *Dilophosaurus* could spit venom or even some type of "fire."

Although *Dilophosaurus* walked on its two hind legs, it also had long upper arms. They had four fingers on each hand, but only three of the fingers had a claw attached. The dual crests that ran the length of the skull were quite thin, and they were probably designed for ornamentation or to attract a mate. The crests did not seem to provide any sort of protection.

Dilophosaurus
dye-LOF-uh-SAWR-us

NECK FRILL?

Dilophosaurus has been portrayed with a retractable neck frill that it could extend if agitated. However, paleontologists have not found scientific evidence that this or any dinosaur had a neck frill. And if they did have them, without a living *Dilophosaurus* to observe, we would not be able to know for sure why they would have extended them. In short, we cannot always trust how dinosaurs are portrayed in popular culture and even in museums.

"TWO-CRESTED"

Dilophosaurus means "two-crested reptile," and it was first described in 1954 from partial skeletons found in 1942. Paleontologist Samuel Paul Welles originally named this dinosaur *Megalosaurus*, thinking it was similar to a previously named dinosaur found in Britain. However, after finding more skeletal remains at the Arizona site in 1964, he renamed the dinosaur *Dilophosaurus* in 1970.

Dilophosaurus is distinguished by the dual, thin, bony crests that run along the top of its skull. The adults grew to about 20 feet in length and may have weighed between 1,000 and 2,000 pounds. Its sharp blade-like teeth show a distinct gap in the upper jaw between the front (premaxillary) teeth and the cheek (maxillary) teeth. *Dilophosaurus* is classified in the infraorder Ceratosauridae ("horned lizards") due to its crested skull.

LAND AND SEA CREATURES BURIED TOGETHER

The Kayenta Formation in Arizona contains not just the remains of *Dilophosaurus*, but of other dinosaurs and even fossil sharks, bony fish, bivalves, and snails. Paleontologists have also found crocodiles, turtles, mammals, other species of dinosaurs, and even a pterosaur (flying retile) in the same rock formation. How did land animals end up with marine animals? It seems that during the great Flood of Noah's day, the Kayenta Formation was formed by tsunami-like waves mixing various animals from the ocean and land with sand and silt, then spreading them in a muddy deposit across what is now Arizona. This resulted in the well-mixed siltstone layer that we see today.

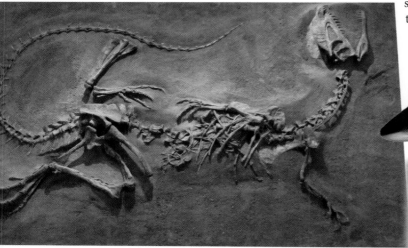

Dilophosaurus cast on display at the Royal Ontario Museum.

THE KAYENTA FORMATION

The Kayenta Formation is a rock formation that spreads across parts of Arizona, Colorado, Nevada, and Utah. Its layers are typically red to brown in color. *Dilophosaurus* was discovered in a portion of the Kayenta Formation in Arizona in 1942.

Kayenta Formation, Arizona

Suborder Sauropodomorpha: The Large and Lumbering

The sauropodomorphs were the longest and heaviest animals to ever walk the earth. Some were at least 140 feet long and could grow possibly up to 160 feet. Paleontologists estimate that they weighed 44 to 55 tons, with some weighing as much as 110 tons. They had ten or more elongated vertebrae in the neck—hence their common title of "long-necks"—and most had an equally long tail. Their massive leg bones and a thickening of the cushioning cartilage between their joints supported their massive weight. Sauropodomorphs had rather small heads compared to their body size and walked on short, compact feet, like elephants, with a large claw on the first digit (the big toe) of the front feet. All of these dinosaurs are thought to be exclusively plant-eaters since many did not have sharp teeth.

Two sauropod families common to North America are the Camarasauridae and the Diplodocidae. The camarasaurs had spoon-shape teeth that ran the entire length of the jaw. The diplodocids had only front teeth that were peg-shaped, most likely for stripping vegetation from branches. Camarasaurs also had a blunt, rounded skull, and diplodocids had an elongated, horse-like skull. Neither type had room for much of a brain.

INFRAORDERS

Sauropodomorphs are divided into two infraorders: 1) prosauropods and 2) sauropods. Prosauropods were smaller and shorter than other sauropods. Many were less than 25 feet long, and some may have walked bipedally. They also differed from sauropods in that they had a small fifth digit on their hind feet. Paleontologists have found prosauropod fossils on six continents, including Antarctica. Sauropods are the more well-known of the sauropodomorphs. These include *Apatosaurus, Brachiosaurus, Diplodocus,* and *Camarasaurus.* Sauropods had holes called pleurocoels on the side of their back vertebrae. These openings lessened the weight of the vertebrae, making them more mobile. Sauropods have been found on every continent.

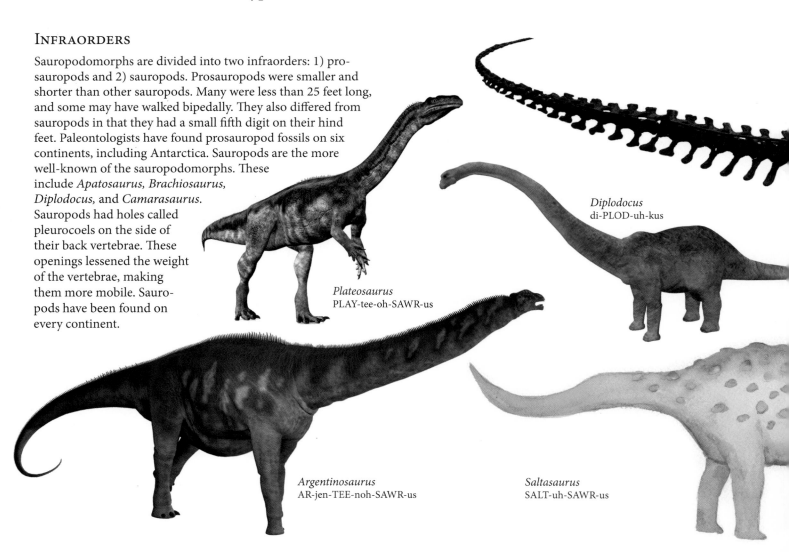

Plateosaurus
PLAY-tee-oh-SAWR-us

Diplodocus
di-PLOD-uh-kus

Argentinosaurus
AR-jen-TEE-noh-SAWR-us

Saltasaurus
SALT-uh-SAWR-us

Missing Skulls

Sauropods are commonly found without a skull. Two reasons for this are the weak attachment sites of the skull on the neck and the fact that the skull bones are thinner and harder to preserve.

Camarasaurus skull
kuh-MARE-uh-SAWR-us

Diplodocus skull
di-PLOD-uh-kus

Arch Design

Engineers fully appreciate the arch, which humans have used in constructing buildings, bridges, and other structures for millennia. An arch is a self-supporting span that stretches over a space. The rounded part of the arch distributes the weight above it to the side supports, creating an efficient support system.

Sauropod spines are perfectly designed arches that distribute the dinosaurs' weight evenly to their feet, which act like the supports. This structural system works in concert with specially designed muscles and tendons in the dinosaurs' long necks and tails so that they could raise and move their heads with relative ease. Arches show that sauropods—and by extension all living creatures—were engineered with special body designs, and design and engineering requires designers and engineers.

Stone arches of an ancient Roman aqueduct

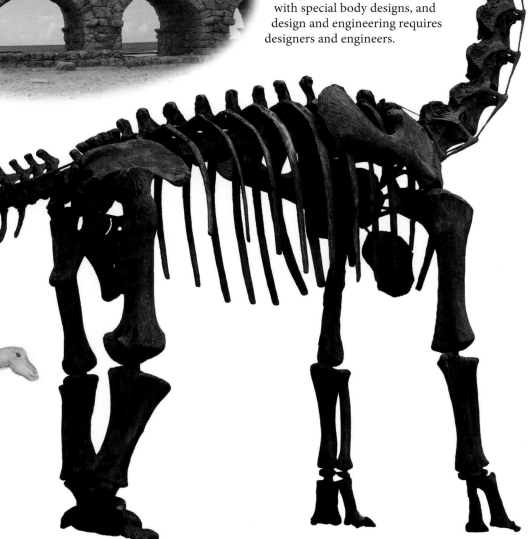

Camarasaurus: The Blunt-Nose Giant

Camarasaurus is among the most common of the sauropod fossils, which paleontologists find mostly in North America. Compared to other sauropods, *Camarasaurus* had a relatively short neck and a short tail. It also had a relatively small head, a short, blunt snout, and spoon-shape teeth that lined its jaws, which probably allowed it to eat coarser vegetation like tree bark. Paleontologists estimate, based on fossil evidence, that *Camarasaurus* adults could grow to about 60 feet in length and weigh almost 20 tons.

The first *Camarasaurus* bones were a few vertebrae found in the Morrison Formation in Colorado in 1877. Famed dinosaur hunter Edward Drinker Cope, in his ongoing Bone Wars with fellow hunter Othniel Charles Marsh, purchased the bones and gave the dinosaur the name *Camarasaurus supremus* that same year.

"Chambered Lizard"

Cope named this dinosaur *Camarasaurus* ("chambered lizard") because of the hollow chambers in its vertebrae, which were the only bones he was able to analyze in the beginning. These hollows, also called pleurocoels, lightened the neck and tail so they could be suspended in the air with ease.

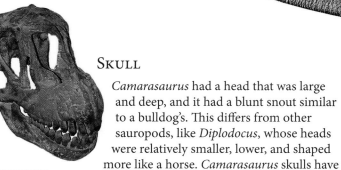

Skull

Camarasaurus had a head that was large and deep, and it had a blunt snout similar to a bulldog's. This differs from other sauropods, like *Diplodocus*, whose heads were relatively smaller, lower, and shaped more like a horse. *Camarasaurus* skulls have large cavities where the eyes and nostrils were once located, so they probably had good sight and smelling capabilities.

Camarasaurus skull

Bulldog

FLEEING THE GREAT FLOOD

Paleontologists have found *Camarasaurus* eggs that were laid in a linear fashion before they were buried and preserved in mud that quickly (in a matter of days or weeks) dried and hardened into rock. A *Camarasaurus* had likely laid the eggs while it was walking and left them behind. Some researchers believe that this find shows that *Camarasaurus* did not raise its own young.

However, just as with all dinosaur behavior, no one can know for certain how *Camarasaurus* parented without observing a living one. What we can observe is that laying eggs in a linear pattern is unusual for most living reptiles. Mother crocodiles, snakes, and lizards usually find or dig a partially covered hole on land in which to lay their eggs. Then, they wait nearby to protect the nest until the eggs hatch. Sea turtles will usually abandon their eggs, but not before laying them in a nest and burying them. What probably happened with these dinosaur eggs is that the mother *Camarasaurus* was trying to escape from the rising waters during the time of Noah's Flood. Out of time and unable to find a safe nest in which to lay the eggs, she probably laid her eggs while fleeing in an effort to save her life.

Crocodile eggs

Camarasaurus
kuh-MARE-uh-SAWR-us

Brachiosaurus: The Big-Nose Giant

Because of a large nasal opening on top of its head, *Brachiosaurus* is sometimes included in a new subcategory of sauropods called Macronaria, which means "big noses." They were a bit different from most sauropods. Because of the large nasal opening on the top of their skulls, early paleontologists believed brachiosaurs lived in water, using it to buoy their massive bodies and breathing out of the barely exposed tips of their skulls. However, later studies of their compact foot structure suggested that they were land-dwellers like most dinosaurs. Dr. Larry Witmer, an American paleontologist, suggested that the nose openings on these dinosaurs were closer to the front of the skull and filled with fleshy nasal tissue, giving them an increased sense of smell.

Brachiosaurus is one of the heaviest and strangest sauropod dinosaurs. It is estimated to have weighed up to 50 tons with a length of 85 feet. The strangest feature is not its bulbous nose but its front legs, which were longer than its hind legs. This caused the animal to hold its head up extremely high in the air, possibly up to 60 feet above the ground! Paleontologists still struggle to explain the blood pressure necessary to supply the brain at such a great height.

Elmer Riggs and H. W. Menke working on *Brachiosaurus altithorax* bones

In 1900, *Brachiosaurus altithorax* was found in western Colorado by Elmer Riggs of the University of Chicago. He recovered about 20% of the specimen, including some of the leg bones, ribs, pelvis and vertebrae—just enough material to name the new species the "arm lizard" in honor of its long front legs. Today, most of the original specimen is stashed out of public view at the Field Museum of Natural History in Chicago, but replicas are on display outside the Field Museum and in Chicago's O'Hare International Airport.

A more complete *Brachiosaurus* specimen was described by Werner Janensch in 1914 after German expeditions to Tanzania in 1909–1912. American paleontologists were able to take bone replicas from this find and construct and mount their original *Brachiosaurus*. Recently, the Tanzanian specimen, housed at the Berlin Museum, was renamed *Giraffatitan brancai* due to slight differences in bone proportions. Creation scientists, by contrast, consider both of these species—and subsequent species—of brachiosaurs the same "kind" and attribute any minor differences to being merely variations in God's well-designed brachiosaur theme.

Surprisingly, German geophysicist and meteorologist Alfred Wegener never mentioned the co-discovery of brachiosaurs in North America and in Africa as evidence to support his fledgling hypothesis of continental drift. He mentioned other fossils that "matched" when he reconstructed his visionary Pangaea (the idea that all continents were a single land mass at one point in time) but seemed to miss this opportunity to further boost his idea. Paleontologists of the day probably wondered how the same dinosaur could have co-existed on two continents now separated by thousands of miles of ocean. It wasn't until the modern theory of plate tectonics came about that this mystery was resolved.

Alfred Wegener

Brachiosaurus
BRACK-ee-uh-SAWR-us

Another Macronarian dinosaur was found in the African nation of Niger by Paul Sereno. He named this dinosaur *Jobaria*, meaning "mythical animal." He found close to 95% of the type specimen along with a juvenile of the same species, but neither had a skull. Sereno finally located a seemingly correct skull miles away with the help of a local nomad. The adult *Jobaria* was approximately 70 feet long and weighed about 25 tons.

Diplodocus: The Great American Dinosaur

On July 4, 1899, a team from the Carnegie Institute in Pittsburgh (now the Carnegie Museum of Natural History) found a toe bone of a large sauropod dinosaur near Como Bluff, Wyoming. They kept digging and soon realized they had a nearly complete skeleton of an 84-foot *Diplodocus* they nicknamed "Dippy." Classifying this as a new species, they named it *Diplodocus carnegii* after Andrew Carnegie, their benefactor who was sponsoring the expedition. The first *Diplodocus* had been named earlier, in 1878, by Othniel Charles Marsh, who studied a specimen from Cañon City, Colorado. This first specimen and Dippy were both found in the same rock layer, the Morrison Formation, although in different states.

Once back in Pittsburgh, the Carnegie team quickly mounted the new *Diplodocus carnegii* in their museum for the world to see. This was one of the first and longest dinosaurs ever placed on public display. The demand was unprecedented. Andrew Carnegie even had to hire a special team to make plaster reproductions of his new dinosaur to meet the demand for copies. Over the next few years, replicas of this sauropod were distributed to nearly all the prominent museums of the world, from Europe to South America, and Dippy is often credited with jumpstarting the popularity of dinosaurs.

Mounted *D. carnegii* holotype skeleton, Carnegie Museum of Natural History

Diplodocus means "double beam." It was given this name because this sauropod had two parallel rods arranged in a mirror-image fashion as chevrons along the underside of the tail. The tail was composed of at least 80 separate vertebrae, and the last 30 vertebrae were rods that got progressively thinner, creating a whip-like end. Some paleontologists have suggested these tails could be rapidly snapped like a whip, creating a cracking sound for warning the herd.

When found, sauropod skeletons are usually missing the skulls. It is fairly common in paleontology to find an entire neck and body but not the skull. Evolutionary scientists think flowing water caused the head, which wasn't well attached to begin with, to separate from the body before it was buried. Creation scientists agree with this interpretation to some extent, except they see the water transport as a consequence of the worldwide Flood and not just a local flood event.

Diplodocus skull

With weight estimates ranging from 10 to 18 tons, diplodocids were rather slender for sauropods. Their limb bones were more lanky than those of many sauropods, and their ribs were long and narrow. By contrast, *Brachiosaurus* probably weighed in at closer to 40 to 50 tons.

The design of *Diplodocus* teeth makes this animal perfectly suited for eating soft plants and stripping leaves and needles from branches. Diplodocids had only peg-shape front teeth, top and bottom, with no molars to chew with. They likely relied on gastroliths (stomach stones) in a special gizzard, their lower stomach's muscle pouch, in order to digest their food.

There are four accepted species of *Diplodocus*. The first is called *Diplodocus longus*. All of the specimens are essentially the same, with only slight differences. Creation scientists consider these all versions of one kind, somewhat like breeds of dogs. It is likely that sauropod dinosaurs like the *Mamenchisaurus* from China and the *Seismosaurus* from New Mexico are also variations of this same kind.

Seismosaurus
SISE-mo-SAWR-us

Mamenchisaurus
mah-MEN-kee-SAWR-us

Diplodocus
di-PLOD-uh-kus

Plateosaurus: The Flat Lizard

*P*lateosaurus was a long-necked dinosaur and a member of the prosauropoda infraorder. It had a small head and a bulky body, along with large hind legs and shorter forelimbs. Paleontologists estimate from fossils that *Plateosaurus* could grow to over 30 feet in length and could probably have weighed well over four tons.

Plateosaurus would have walked on all fours and on its toes, but it probably could also stand on its hind legs and grasp onto tree trunks and other tall objects with its long thumbclaws. *Plateosaurus* had flat-sided, leaf-shape teeth that were ideal for sawing through vegetation, but it may also have swallowed small stones (gastroliths) to further grind up plant matter in its stomach so that it could digest its food easier.

Plateosaurus had leaf-shape serrated teeth that acted like saws on the rough vegetation it ate.

"Flat Lizard"

Fossilized vertebrae and leg bones from the dinosaur were first discovered in Germany in 1834. The name *Plateosaurus* may mean either "flat lizard" or "broad lizard," and it is unclear why it was given this name.

German paleontologist Hermann von Meyer published a description of *Plateosaurus* in 1855, along with illustrations, but he did not write about the meaning behind the dinosaur's name. Since its initial discovery, the partial to complete remains of over 100 *Plateosaurus* individuals have been uncovered in various parts of Europe.

Hermann von Meyer

Plateosaurus
PLAY-tee-oh-SAWR-us

BURIED TOGETHER

Paleontologists have found several *Plateosaurus* individuals buried together in parts of Europe. This could show that these dinosaurs lived in herds, similar to cattle and elephants. It could also indicate they were fleeing the rising waters of the great Flood of Noah's day.

Fossils form when creatures are rapidly buried in water and sediments (mud) before their bodies can be scavenged by predators. Minerals in the water cause the material to harden like cement. This helps to preserve the buried creatures from water-borne bacteria that would otherwise decompose the remains.

CLASSIFICATION PROBLEMS

Plateosaurus has been reclassified several times since its discovery in the mid-1800s. Hermann von Meyer once had it categorized in a now defunct group, and Othniel Charles Marsh placed it with the theropods (*Tyrannosaurus, Velociraptor,* etc.). *Plateosaurus* is now classified with Sauropodomorpha because it is believed to be similar to the sauropods, although even evolutionists disagree on this.

The confusion surrounding *Plateosaurus*' classification can stem from disagreements among scientists on where it fell in the line of dinosaur evolution. However, if *Plateosaurus* was just a variation within a uniquely created dinosaur kind, then classifying it should not be as confusing.

Brontosaurus or *Apatosaurus*?

During the Bone Wars between dinosaur hunters Othniel Charles Marsh and Edward Drinker Cope, many mistakes were made in the naming of dinosaurs. The most famous is the controversy over *Brontosaurus* that became well-known with the issuing of four dinosaur stamps. In 1989, the U.S. Postal Service created stamps that included *Tyrannosaurus, Stegosaurus, Brontosaurus,* and the winged reptile *Pteranodon*. Concerned citizens wrote to the Postal Service explaining that *Brontosaurus* should have been called *Apatosaurus* on the stamp, since the two are the same creature and *Apatosaurus* was named first.

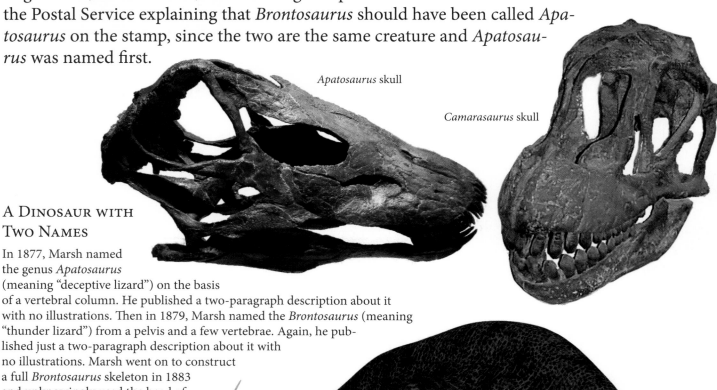

Apatosaurus skull

Camarasaurus skull

A Dinosaur with Two Names

In 1877, Marsh named the genus *Apatosaurus* (meaning "deceptive lizard") on the basis of a vertebral column. He published a two-paragraph description about it with no illustrations. Then in 1879, Marsh named the *Brontosaurus* (meaning "thunder lizard") from a pelvis and a few vertebrae. Again, he published just a two-paragraph description about it with no illustrations. Marsh went on to construct a full *Brontosaurus* skeleton in 1883 and unknowingly used the head of a *Camarasaurus* by mistake. The *Brontosaurus* went on to become even more popular when it appeared as the Sinclair Oil symbol and in several movies.

In 1903, after Marsh passed away, Elmer Riggs at the Field Columbian Museum in Chicago (now the Field Museum of Natural History) issued a proclamation in a rather obscure journal that the *Apatosaurus* Marsh named was actually a juvenile *Brontosaurus* specimen. Riggs concluded that the name *Brontosaurus* should be dropped in favor of the first scientific name issued: *Apatosaurus*.

Apatosaurus
uh-PAT-uh-SAWR-us

1989 U.S. Post Office Stamp

The U.S. Postal Service responded to the *Brontosaurus* name controversy with Bulletin 21744, invoking the Plenary Powers Rule that says popularized names can be validated even if older designations have priority. In other words, if a name is popular, it can still be scientifically correct. So, *Brontosaurus* is as correct to use as *Apatosaurus* for this genus, and the stamps and name were saved from destruction.

USA 25 *Brontosaurus*

"Deceptive Lizard"

The name *Apatosaurus* means "deceptive lizard." Looking back at all the controversy involved with this dinosaur, it seems appropriate that Marsh named this dinosaur what he did.

Camarasaurus
kuh-MARE-uh-SAWR-us

Camarasaurus

Marsh used the head of a nearby *Camarasaurus* in his reconstruction of a *Brontosaurus* skeleton in 1883. Most sauropod dinosaurs are found without heads because they had weak attachment sites on the neck, and Marsh had simply grabbed the closest head he could find to complete the skeleton. Due to the popularity of the *Brontosaurus* and the number of museums with copies of it, correcting this mistake took nearly 100 years, and it continues to this day!

Apatosaurus

Suborder Marginocephalia: The Domed, Horned, and Frilled

The term Marginocephalia means "edge head," and all of the dinosaurs in this suborder had some type of frill or ridge along the back of the skull. This suborder is divided into two rather diverse infraorders—the Pachycephalosauria and the Ceratopsia.

Pachycephalosauria means "dome head," and this group consisted of bipedal, dome-headed dinosaurs with a thickened bone on the roof of the skull. The most common dinosaur from this group is the genus *Stegoceras*, which is found in North America. Other pachycephalosaur fossil fragments have been found in Europe and Asia.

Ceratopsia means "horn head," and this infraorder is further divided into the groups Psittacosauridae and Neoceratopsia. The Psittacosauridae is represented by the genus *Psittacosaurus*, which is a bipedal dinosaur also known as the "parrot lizard." Neoceratopsia includes the horned and frilled dinosaurs such as *Triceratops, Styracosaurus,* and *Centrosaurus,* which paleontologists discovered in North America. Neoceratopsia also includes the protoceratopsids, which had no pronounced horns on the head, that have been found primarily in Asia. Ceratopsia was one of the most diverse groups of dinosaurs in terms of the variety of horn and frill styles and shapes, and the group most likely reflects variations within one of the created dinosaur kinds.

PACHYCEPHALOSAURIA

Stegoceras, like all Pachycephalosauria, had small, serrated teeth for eating and slicing vegetation. The skull attached to the neck at an angle to the backbone so that the head hung down and the top of the domed skull was out front and pointed forward. These dinosaurs had many similar body features in common with ornithopods (duck-billed dinosaurs). They had much longer hind limbs and a tail with ossified tendons for support. Most paleontologists think the domed head was used for competition within the species, like bighorn sheep today. It may have been used as a defense when threatened or simply for display.

Stegoceras
STEG-uh-SEHR-us

CERATOPSIA

Most Ceratopsia were large, around 20 to 30 feet long. They ate plants, walked on all four limbs, and had extremely large skulls (up to eight feet long). They also had a wide variety of horn and frill shapes. The basic body structure of all of these dinosaurs was the same design, and they probably even looked identical as hatchlings. When they matured, however, the differences in horn and frill shape became evident. They had toothless, beaked jaws with brackets of cheek teeth similar to hadrosaurs, including three to four replacement teeth below the active teeth on top. The teeth came together at a high angle, producing a scissor-like motion. Combined with the large frills for jaw muscle attachment, these dinosaurs could chew up the coarsest of plant material.

Torosaurus
TOR-uh-SAWR-us

FRILL

Many paleontologists used to think the frill was used for protection from predation, but after careful examination that seems less likely. First, the frills usually had large holes in them, which does not serve for much protection. Secondly, the frills had lots of blood vessels and were filled with internal openings, similar to stegosaur plates. That means that they likely bled if broken or bitten. Most paleontologists now think the frills were for muscle attachment, giving the creature a strong bite.

Triceratops skull
try-SEH-ruh-tops

Protoceratops
pro-toe-SEH-ruh-tops

Psittacosaurus
SIT-eh-kuh-SAWR-us

Pachycephalosaurus
PACK-ee-SEF-uh-luh-SAWR-us

Protoceratops: The "Sheep" of Ceratopsian Dinosaurs

During the first Central Asiatic Expedition to Mongolia in 1922, expedition photographer J. B. Shackelford discovered a dinosaur skull. Walter Granger and W. K. Gregory described this new dinosaur—calling it *Protoceratops andrewsi* in honor of the expedition leader, Roy Chapman Andrews. The name means "first horned face." Shackelford also found eggshell fragments in the same area that were thought to be from a prehistoric bird.

The following year, the second Asiatic expedition found egg nests in clusters of up to 13. Because they found 70 skulls and 14 skeletons of *Protoceratops* in the same rock layers as the eggs, they naturally assumed the eggs were also *Protoceratops*. However, in 1993 an embryonic skeleton was discovered in a similar egg showing that it was an *Oviraptor* egg and not *Protoceratops*. The so-called egg-stealing dinosaur (*Oviraptor*) was shown to be the parent dinosaur, and all the eggs are now attributed to *Oviraptor*.

A sheep-size dinosaur weighing up to 400 pounds, *Protoceratops* stood two to three feet high and was about five to six feet long. Based on the numbers of skeletons found in single locations in Mongolia and China, evolutionary scientists believe this dinosaur herded in large numbers, gaining it the reputation as the sheep of dinosaurs. However, creation scientists explain part of this apparent herding as a consequence of catastrophic Flood activity, where tsunami-like waves pushed dinosaur carcasses together in massive deposits, giving the appearance of herd behavior. Later expeditions by the American Museum of Natural History found a variety of other animals mixed in the layers with the *Protoceratops* fossils, including crocodiles, turtles, and even *Velociraptor* fossils.

Many *Protoceratops* skulls have large frills while others have short compact frills on the back of the skull. Some paleontologists think these two sizes may be related to physical differences in the sexes. Some believe the larger-frilled specimens are males and the smaller are females. Since there is no clear way to differentiate the sexes from most fossils, this matter still remains unresolved.

Protoceratops
pro-toe-SEH-ruh-tops

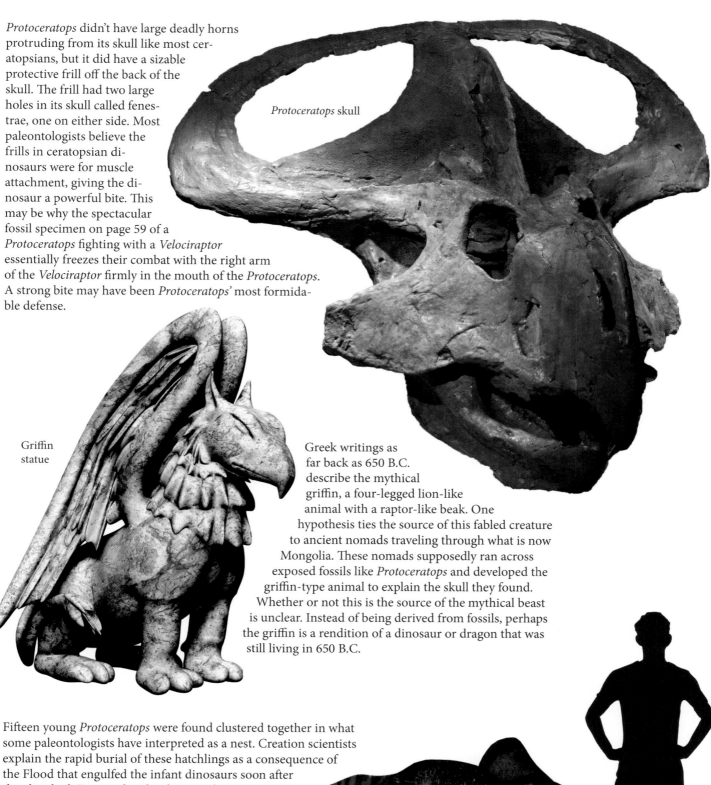

Protoceratops didn't have large deadly horns protruding from its skull like most ceratopsians, but it did have a sizable protective frill off the back of the skull. The frill had two large holes in its skull called fenestrae, one on either side. Most paleontologists believe the frills in ceratopsian dinosaurs were for muscle attachment, giving the dinosaur a powerful bite. This may be why the spectacular fossil specimen on page 59 of a *Protoceratops* fighting with a *Velociraptor* essentially freezes their combat with the right arm of the *Velociraptor* firmly in the mouth of the *Protoceratops*. A strong bite may have been *Protoceratops'* most formidable defense.

Protoceratops skull

Griffin statue

Greek writings as far back as 650 B.C. describe the mythical griffin, a four-legged lion-like animal with a raptor-like beak. One hypothesis ties the source of this fabled creature to ancient nomads traveling through what is now Mongolia. These nomads supposedly ran across exposed fossils like *Protoceratops* and developed the griffin-type animal to explain the skull they found. Whether or not this is the source of the mythical beast is unclear. Instead of being derived from fossils, perhaps the griffin is a rendition of a dinosaur or dragon that was still living in 650 B.C.

Fifteen young *Protoceratops* were found clustered together in what some paleontologists have interpreted as a nest. Creation scientists explain the rapid burial of these hatchlings as a consequence of the Flood that engulfed the infant dinosaurs soon after they hatched. During the Flood, many dinosaurs survived for some time, constantly seeking higher ground, before they succumbed to the rising waters. Stressed pregnant dinosaurs would have followed their instincts, made nests, and laid eggs on the increasingly limited dry land available. Because of the global nature of this catastrophe, we find dinosaur eggs, nests, young hatchlings, juveniles, and adults—every stage of life—all preserved as fossils in Flood deposits around the world.

Pachycephalosaurus: The Dome-Heads

The first specimens of the infraorder Pachycephalosauria, or "dome-headed reptiles," were found in the 1850s, but many of these were labeled as completely different species due to the lack of fossil material. Mostly, what is found is the thickened skull cap—the dome—and little else. Because of the fragmentary nature of the discoveries, some of these dinosaurs were even confused with the theropod *Troodon*, which has similar teeth. This group contains 11 species discovered across the northern hemisphere throughout North America, Europe, and Asia. Their fossils are found in later Flood rocks that are labeled as upper Cretaceous system strata.

Pachycephalosaurs walked on two legs, were about six to seven feet long, and most weighed under 200 pounds. The design of these dinosaurs included stiffening at the end of the tail caused by ossified tendons that curbed flexibility—similar to ornithopods and dromaeosaurs. The tail likely functioned with limited side-to-side motion as a counterweight for balance when walking and running.

The dome was usually smooth on the top, but many species had pointy bumps sticking out around the back and sides. Most pachycephalosaurs also had a small rim or shelf on the back of their skulls. Because of this small ridge, many paleontologists lump them into the suborder Marginocephalia ("ridge-headed") with the ceratopsians like *Triceratops* and *Protoceratops*.

Pachycephalosaurus skull

Pachycephalosaurs had some of the most diverse teeth of all the dinosaurs. The teeth in the front upper jaw were cone-shape, and teeth on the sides of the jaws were leaf-shape with ridges. Some species also had cone-shape teeth in their lower jaw. This variety means these dinosaurs probably ate a wide range of plants and vegetation.

Fossils from the *Stegoceras* genus are among the most commonly found from the Pachycephalosauria order. About 40 partial specimens have been found in western North America in rock units like the Hell Creek Formation in Montana.

Stegoceras skull

Stegoceras
STEG-uh-SEHR-us

Pachycephalosaurus bones were first discovered by geologist Ferdinand V. Hayden in eastern Montana in 1859 to 1860. It wasn't until after Barnum Brown co-established the genus *Pachycephalosaurus* in 1943 that these earlier bones were found to be the same species. Unfortunately, even today, scientists aren't sure what a complete *Pachycephalosaurus* should look like since most finds are just a skullcap and a few broken pieces. These dinosaurs may have been larger than other genera in the Pachycephalosauria order—up to 15 feet long and weighing close to 900 pounds.

DID YOU KNOW?

A fossilized skull found in South Dakota's Hell Creek Formation was treated as a new genus of dinosaur and named *Dracorex hogwartsia* in honor of the school in J. K. Rowlings' Harry Potter books. However, scientists are now saying this skull actually represents a juvenile *Pachycephalosaurus* specimen rather than a separate genus.

Dracorex hogwartsia
DRAY-coh-rex hog-WART-see-uh

Pachycephalosaurus
PACK-ee-SEF-uh-luh-SAWR-us

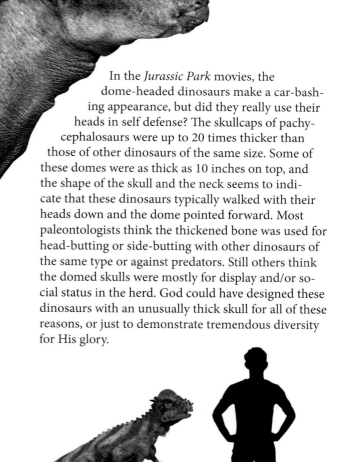

In the *Jurassic Park* movies, the dome-headed dinosaurs make a car-bashing appearance, but did they really use their heads in self defense? The skullcaps of pachycephalosaurs were up to 20 times thicker than those of other dinosaurs of the same size. Some of these domes were as thick as 10 inches on top, and the shape of the skull and the neck seems to indicate that these dinosaurs typically walked with their heads down and the dome pointed forward. Most paleontologists think the thickened bone was used for head-butting or side-butting with other dinosaurs of the same type or against predators. Still others think the domed skulls were mostly for display and/or social status in the herd. God could have designed these dinosaurs with an unusually thick skull for all of these reasons, or just to demonstrate tremendous diversity for His glory.

Psittacosaurus: **The Parrot Reptile**

All ceratopsian dinosaurs, like the great-horned *Psittacosaurus,* had an extra beak-like bone in the front of the jaw called a rostral. This "beak bone" fit between the normal premaxillary (front jaw) bones. Psittacosaurs had a pronounced "beak bone" and are classified with the ceratopsians, but they didn't possess frills on the back of their heads like most species in this group, nor did they have prominent horns.

Psittacosaurus is the best-known dinosaur in this group. Its name literally means "parrot reptile" because its facial profile looks like a parrot. Its jaw was unusual for dinosaurs because instead of having a segmented jaw with internal jaw joints, it had a single upper jawbone and a single lower jawbone. The beak was rounded and flattened and seems to have been designed for cropping vegetation. Fossils show that it had collagenous fibers sticking up from its tail.

Psittacosaurus was first found in Mongolia during the Central Asiatic Expedition led by Roy Chapman Andrews in 1922. Henry Fairfield Osborn from the American Museum of Natural History named the species in 1923. Although about five to seven feet in length, an adult *Psittacosaurus* only weighed about 50 pounds. Over 400 specimens of the psittacosaurs—and at least 10 species—have been found with sizes ranging from six-inch hatchlings to adults. All were likely the same biblical kind since the special differences were quite subtle. The psittacosaurids are found in later Flood rocks identified as lower Cretaceous system strata.

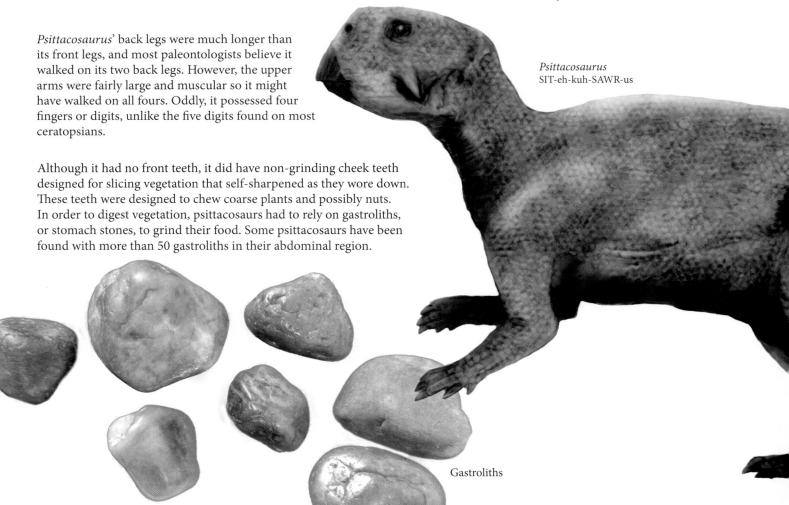

Psittacosaurus' back legs were much longer than its front legs, and most paleontologists believe it walked on its two back legs. However, the upper arms were fairly large and muscular so it might have walked on all fours. Oddly, it possessed four fingers or digits, unlike the five digits found on most ceratopsians.

Psittacosaurus
SIT-eh-kuh-SAWR-us

Although it had no front teeth, it did have non-grinding cheek teeth designed for slicing vegetation that self-sharpened as they wore down. These teeth were designed to chew coarse plants and possibly nuts. In order to digest vegetation, psittacosaurs had to rely on gastroliths, or stomach stones, to grind their food. Some psittacosaurs have been found with more than 50 gastroliths in their abdominal region.

Gastroliths

Crocodile

The *Psittacosaurus'* flexible tail has caused some paleontologists to suggest this animal was aquatic or semi-aquatic, using its tail like a crocodile—swinging it from side to side as it swam. The collagenous fibers of its bristled tail may have been designed to stick above the water, serving as a fin-like apparatus.

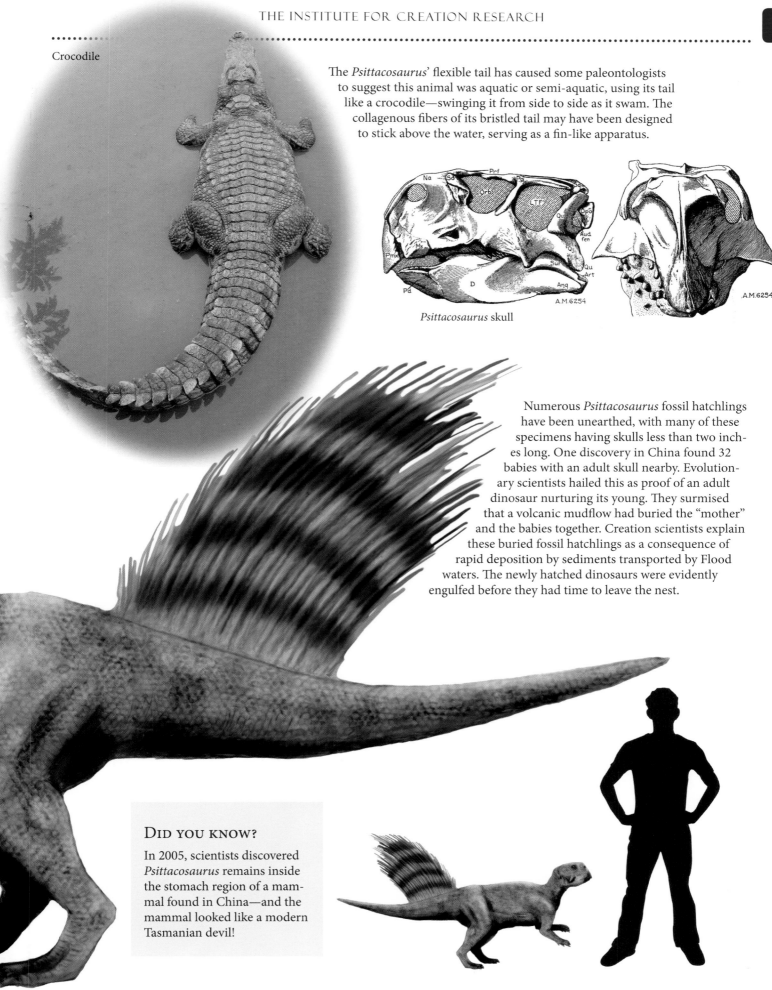

Psittacosaurus skull

Numerous *Psittacosaurus* fossil hatchlings have been unearthed, with many of these specimens having skulls less than two inches long. One discovery in China found 32 babies with an adult skull nearby. Evolutionary scientists hailed this as proof of an adult dinosaur nurturing its young. They surmised that a volcanic mudflow had buried the "mother" and the babies together. Creation scientists explain these buried fossil hatchlings as a consequence of rapid deposition by sediments transported by Flood waters. The newly hatched dinosaurs were evidently engulfed before they had time to leave the nest.

DID YOU KNOW?

In 2005, scientists discovered *Psittacosaurus* remains inside the stomach region of a mammal found in China—and the mammal looked like a modern Tasmanian devil!

Styracosaurus: The Spiked Dinosaur

Styracosaurus was a plant-eating dinosaur that walked on all four limbs and had a frill on its neck with bony spikes. It also had a horn on its nose and smaller horns above its eyes. While the neck frill and horns are similar to those of other ceratopsian dinosaurs, the spikes on the frill were unique to *Styracosaurus*. The spikes grew out of small bony knobs called epoccipital bones on the dinosaur's frill. These dinosaurs may have grown up to 18 feet long and weighed between 2.5 and 3 tons.

Styracosaurus had a strong beak-like tip on its mouth, which it probably used to grasp and pluck at the tough vegetation it ate. It also had sets of replaceable teeth that were shaped more for slicing rather than grinding, which they would have needed to bite through plants like palms and ferns.

Styracosaurus
stye-RAK-uh-SAWR-us

"SPIKED LIZARD"

Charles M. Sternberg, one of the sons of dinosaur hunter Charles Sternberg, first discovered fossil remains of *Styracosaurus* in what is now known as the Dinosaur Park Formation in Alberta, Canada, in 1913. Paleontologist Lawrence M. Lambe named it *Styracosaurus* (meaning "spiked lizard") that same year because of the spikes that grew from its neck frill. The spikes were unique to this dinosaur and may have had a variety of purposes, such as knocking down tall plants for food, defense against predators, or to compete for a mate. Like other ceratopsian dinosaurs, *Styracosaurus* had a sturdy body design similar to rhinoceroses. It probably charged its opponents head-on, inflicting much damage with its horn.

Styracosaurus skull

DINOSAUR PARK FORMATION

Dinosaur Park Formation is located in Dinosaur Provincial Park, a UNESCO Heritage Site located near Calgary, Alberta, Canada. Dinosaur hunters have found the remains of various dinosaurs in the formation, such as ankylosaurs, ceratopsians, ornithopods, and theropods, including tyrannosaurs. Fossils of other animals, including fish, turtles, and crocodiles, have also been discovered there. Formations containing dinosaur bones often have "modern" animal fossils and plants mixed in with them, showing that these creatures all died and were buried together rapidly in a catastrophic event like the great Flood of Noah's day.

SAME DINOSAUR?

Paleontologists traditionally named new ceratopsian dinosaurs whenever a specimen appeared to have a different number of horns. However, it is possible that some of these were actually the same dinosaur but at different life stages. For instance, some scientists believe that *Styracosaurus, Centrosaurus,* and even *Monoclonius* may have actually been the same dinosaur but at different ages and/or of different genders.

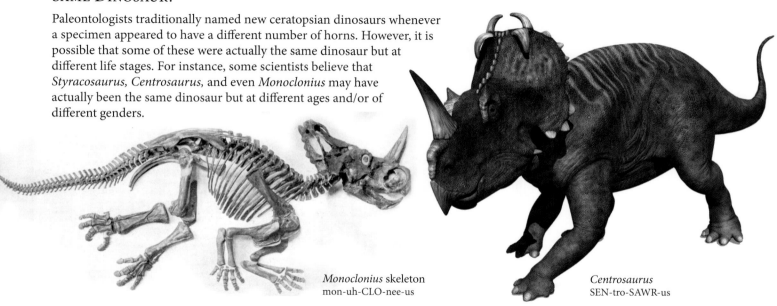

Monoclonius skeleton
mon-uh-CLO-nee-us

Centrosaurus
SEN-tro-SAWR-us

Triceratops: The Three-Horned Dinosaur

*T*riceratops was a plant-eating dinosaur that walked on all four limbs and had a notably large skull that measured about seven to eight feet long. The total length of an adult dinosaur was about 25 to 30 feet. The first four vertebrae of the neck were fused to support the weight of its massive head. The tail was short and narrow, and the pelvis was fused to the backbone, placing the tail in a slight downward position. The four legs of the dinosaur were of near-equal length, suggesting great power and possibly speed when it walked. Footprint evidence suggests that these dinosaurs walked at four to eight mph and might have been able to run as fast as 20 mph.

Triceratops
try-SEH-ruh-tops

Fossil hunters first found *Triceratops* horns attached to part of a skull in 1887 and sent them to paleontologist Othniel Charles Marsh, who thought the horns belonged to an unusually large bison at first. However, more discoveries made him realize the following year that horned dinosaurs had existed, and he wrote about the genus *Ceratops* based on the various fragments. Another skull found in 1888 led Marsh to later change the name to *Triceratops*.

MORTAL COMBAT?

Triceratops have often been depicted fighting epic battles with *Tyrannosaurus*, but did that ever really happen? Amazingly, in 2013 researchers found the fossils of a *Triceratops* and tyrannosaur locked in mortal combat. Tyrannosaur teeth were lodged in the *Triceratops*' skull.

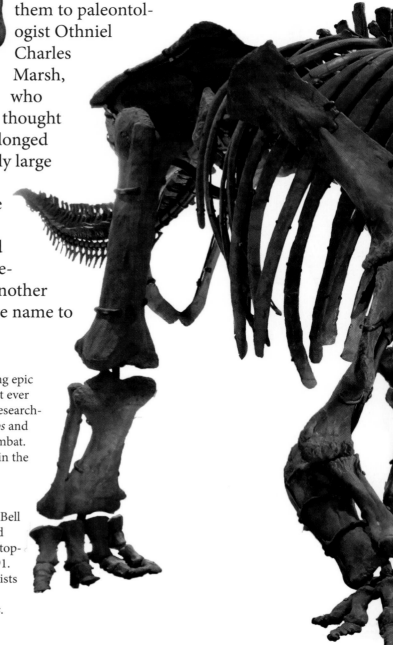

American paleontologist John Bell Hatcher was a fossil hunter and known for discovering the ceratopsian dinosaur *Torosaurus* in 1891. Over 100 years later, some scientists now believe that *Torosaurus* was merely the adult form of *Triceratops*.

John Bell Hatcher

HORNS

Triceratops had two large horns above its eyes and a smaller horn on the tip of its nose. These were different from antlers because they were a permanent part of the skull and made of solid bone. A sheath or covering on the horns that consisted of keratin—similar to fingernail material—sharpened and slightly extended the length of the horns.

Paleontologists thought that *Triceratops* used its horns to counterattack predators like *T. rex*. More recently, based on finding horn marks on the fronts of some neck frills, some scientists believe *Triceratops* and other ceratopsians also used their horns against one another in territorial competitions and to fight over mates.

POSTURE

Scientists have debated for decades the front limb posture of *Triceratops*. Most early reconstructions showed the front limbs sprawling outward from the sides, like a lizard, and the hind legs erect like all dinosaurs. The debate seems to have been settled after the discovery of some ceratopsian footprints in Colorado that indicate an upright posture for both front and hind limbs. Many museum specimens had to be reconstructed to show this upright posture.

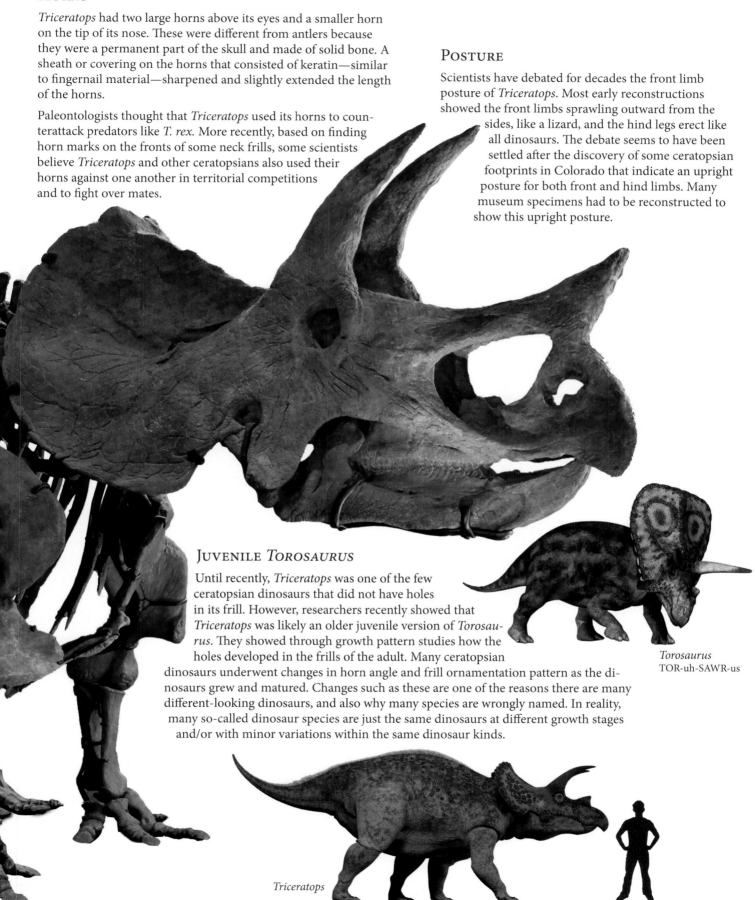

JUVENILE *TOROSAURUS*

Until recently, *Triceratops* was one of the few ceratopsian dinosaurs that did not have holes in its frill. However, researchers recently showed that *Triceratops* was likely an older juvenile version of *Torosaurus*. They showed through growth pattern studies how the holes developed in the frills of the adult. Many ceratopsian dinosaurs underwent changes in horn angle and frill ornamentation pattern as the dinosaurs grew and matured. Changes such as these are one of the reasons there are many different-looking dinosaurs, and also why many species are wrongly named. In reality, many so-called dinosaur species are just the same dinosaurs at different growth stages and/or with minor variations within the same dinosaur kinds.

Torosaurus
TOR-uh-SAWR-us

Triceratops

Suborder Thyreophora: Armored and Plated

Thyreophora means "shield bearers," and these dinosaurs have one or more rows of bony plates embedded in their skin and connective tissue along their backs. All thyreophorans possessed a "bird hip"-style pelvis, and nearly all walked exclusively on four legs. Scientists divide thyreophorans into three groups. The first group is the "primitive" thyreophorans and consists of a few dinosaurs with bony plates, but they had little else in common with the other two groups, stegosaurs and ankylosaurs. The "primitive" designation is an evolutionary reference, although no ancestor/descendant relationships to other thyreophorans have been observed in these dinosaurs.

STEGOSAURS

The second group of thyreophorans were the stegosaurs, meaning "plated lizards." These dinosaurs had a single or double row of vertical plates or spines arranged along their backs. This group includes *Stegosaurus*, *Kentrosaurus*, and *Tuojiangosaurus*.

The plates on the *Stegosaurus* have been the source of much debate. Dinosaur hunter Othniel Charles Marsh arranged the plates in a single row from head to tail, but most paleontologists think there was some degree of overlap between the plates and arranged them in an alternating pattern in two rows. However, the fossils cannot tell researchers which is correct. One clue that may help is the stegosaur-like carving at a temple in Cambodia, which shows a single row down the back. The people who made this carving lived long before modern dinosaur discoveries, and they likely saw what these animals looked like when they were still living.

This carving appears on Ta Prohm, a temple in the Angkor region in Cambodia. The temple was built around the 12th to 13th centuries as a monastery and university. The carving is clearly of a *Stegosaurus* and appears among carvings of other animals that we observe today. The artists who made these carvings likely saw dinosaurs in their lifetimes and were able to depict them in their art.

Stegosaurus
STEG-uh-SAWR-us

Kentrosaurus and *Tuojiangosaurus* differed in design from *Stegosaurus* because they had more spines sticking up along the back and not as many plates. These differences may only have been variations within the created kind. They still had the distinctive fan-shaped body structure of all Stegosauridae, with front legs about half the length of the hind legs, pushing the dinosaur up in the hindquarters.

Kentrosaurus
KEN-troh-SAWR-us

Tuojiangosaurus
toh-ZANG-uh-SAWR-us

ANKYLOSAURS

The third group of thyreophorans were the ankylosaurs, or "fused lizards." They had small heads and leaf-shape, non-connecting teeth similar to the stegosaurs. They differed because they possessed a nearly complete, turtle-like covering of bony plates across their entire upper bodies and backs. Scientists further divide these dinosaurs into the two families Nodosauridae and Ankylosauridae.

Ankylosaurus
ang-KYE-luh-SAWR-us

Nodosaurs differed from ankylosaurs in that they did not have a bony covering on the top of their skulls, and they did not have a tail club. These dinosaurs walked on all four limbs low to the ground, and they were about 18 to 20 feet in length.

Nodosaurus
NODE-oh-SAWR-us

SALTASAURUS

Saltasaurus illustrates the confusion involved in classifying dinosaurs. This dinosaur had several rows of bony plates along its back, which made it fit the definition of a thyreophoran. However, everything else about it fits the definition of a sauropod, including the long neck and tail. Because of this, the definitions of each group have to be refined.

Saltasaurus
salt-uh-SAWR-us

Stegosaurus and Ankylosaurus

The *Stegosaurus* was a low-to-the-ground, plant-eating dinosaur. It grew to be 25 to 30 feet in length and weighed between one and two tons. Its elongated skull had about two-dozen leaf-shape cheek teeth, and instead of front teeth it had a beak. The back legs were twice as long as the front legs, giving the dinosaur a sloped, fan-shape appearance. With the addition of vertical plates protruding along the back, the *Stegosaurus* would have looked much bigger from the side, which would help deter predators. It had four spikes at the end of its tail, each two feet long, which it apparently used for defense.

Like the *Stegosaurus*, *Ankylosaurus* is classified as a thyreophoran, a "shield bearer." Unlike the *Stegosaurus*, this dinosaur had a covering of hard, bony plates and a clubbed tail that made it look like some kind of militarized turtle. The *Ankylosaurus* was not very tall, only about six feet. Its length equaled the *Stegosaurus*—around 25 feet—but it was heavier, weighing between three and six tons. The body armor was fused together in rows that ran down the back and was reinforced by tough outer skin. The head was also covered in bones and had horns pointing backward from the rear corners of the skull. As an herbivore, the *Ankylosaurus* had small, leaf-shape teeth, and fossils show signs of wear and tear probably from chewing vegetation.

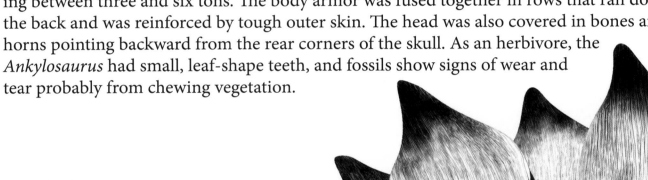

DID YOU KNOW?

The *Stegosaurus* had a brain slightly bigger than a chicken egg, between 2.5 and 3 ounces.

SECOND BRAIN?

For years, scientists pointed to an enlarged cavity in the hind hip region as a possible second brain to help this dinosaur compensate for its small cranial capacity. However, most paleontologists now believe this cavity was used for fat and sugar storage, as seen in some modern birds like ostriches.

Scientists still debate why the *Stegosaurus* had plates on its back. The plates were porous, with many holes and openings for blood vessels. Because of this, many believe that the plates served as heat regulators, like a radiator, where blood could flow in and out to help cool or warm the dinosaur as needed. It is unlikely the plates served any defensive purposes since a predator bite would have caused them to bleed profusely.

Stegosaurus plate

ARMORED TANK

As a sort of reptilian tank, ankylosaurs definitely sacrificed speed for protection. Their four short legs wouldn't let them run from trouble, so they needed to hunker down when attacked, using their tail clubs to counterattack. The clubs were heavy, and the ankylosaurs could whip them with enough force to break the legs of a *T. rex*. Paleontologists discovered one tail club with chips broken off along the edges, evidence of this defensive tactic.

DID YOU KNOW?

The last seven tail vertebrae and several bony plates fused together to make the *Ankylosaurus* club. Although the tail wasn't very flexible, it could still swing about 45 degrees in either direction.

DID YOU KNOW?

The bony plates of the *Ankylosaurus* didn't actually attach to the rest of the skeleton. They grew within the skin and are called osteoderms.

Ankylosaurus
ang-KYE-luh-SAWR-us

Ankylosaurus fossils are found mixed up with marine creatures like sharks and fish, and sometimes are completely upside down. Evolutionists have a hard time explaining these mixtures of land and sea fossils, but creation scientists easily explain that they are a consequence of the global Flood. Tsunami-like waves of the Flood would be expected to wash marine animals onto the continents and create these mixed deposits.

Nodosaurus
NODE-oh-SAWR-us

The *Nodosaurus*, a "shield bearer" thyreophoran, was similar to the *Ankylosaurus*. It had an armor-covered back, but no tail club or armored skull. It may have been a separate biblical kind.

Euoplocephalus
you-op-luh-SEF-uh-lus

The *Euoplocephalus* was slightly shorter in length than the *Ankylosaurus* but had the same sort of bony plates on its back and a clubbed tail. It was likely a member of the same biblical kind.

Stegosaurus
STEG-uh-SAWR-us

Ankylosaurus

Suborder Ornithopoda: The Duck-Bills

The name Ornithopoda means "bird feet" because the hind feet of these dinosaurs left large prints that looked like bird prints. They also had hips that resembled bird hips. Many ornithopods walked on all four legs, though their front legs had small, rather peg-shape feet. The front end of the jaw was set a bit lower than the cheek teeth, giving them a "duck-billed" look.

Three of the ornithopod families—Heterodontosauridae, Hypsilophodontidae, and Dryosauridae—were mostly small (less than 10 feet long), walked on two legs, and were probably fast runners. The most famous ornithopod families, Iguanodontidae and Hadrosauridae, were larger, often 20 to 30 feet long or longer. Their fossils are mostly found in Cretaceous system rocks. These two families had hardened beaks or bills rather than front teeth. Special rod-like tendons along their spine helped stiffen their backs and tails.

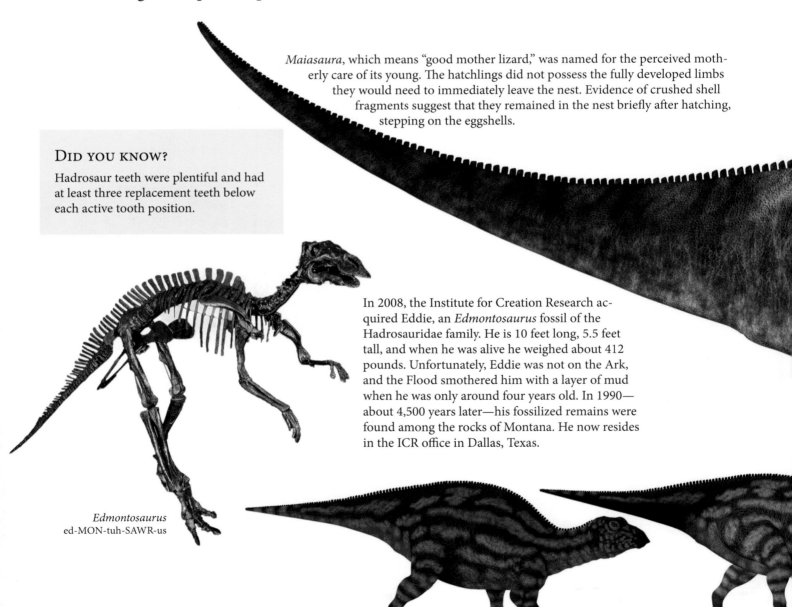

Maiasaura, which means "good mother lizard," was named for the perceived motherly care of its young. The hatchlings did not possess the fully developed limbs they would need to immediately leave the nest. Evidence of crushed shell fragments suggest that they remained in the nest briefly after hatching, stepping on the eggshells.

DID YOU KNOW?

Hadrosaur teeth were plentiful and had at least three replacement teeth below each active tooth position.

In 2008, the Institute for Creation Research acquired Eddie, an *Edmontosaurus* fossil of the Hadrosauridae family. He is 10 feet long, 5.5 feet tall, and when he was alive he weighed about 412 pounds. Unfortunately, Eddie was not on the Ark, and the Flood smothered him with a layer of mud when he was only around four years old. In 1990—about 4,500 years later—his fossilized remains were found among the rocks of Montana. He now resides in the ICR office in Dallas, Texas.

Edmontosaurus
ed-MON-tuh-SAWR-us

The Heterodontosauridae ("different-toothed lizard") family had dinosaurs with cheek teeth and canine-like tusks. Paleontologists have debated what the tusks were used for. Some suggest that they were for display or were only found on males, but there is little data for this. Others think these herbivores may also have eaten meat. Unlike most dinosaurs, heterodontosaurids may have kept their original teeth their whole lives, since CT scans of their skulls have shown no new teeth forming in their jaws.

The Hadrosauridae family further divides into the subfamilies Lambeosaurines and Hadrosaurines. Hadrosaurines had flatter "Roman" noses, while the Lambeosaurines had crests and tubes on top of their heads—like *Parasaurolophus*, which probably made sounds like a trombone to signal danger, distress, group recognition, or mating.

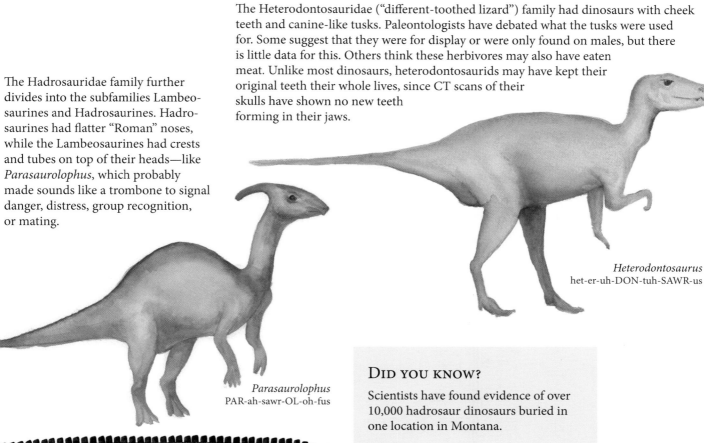

Heterodontosaurus
het-er-uh-DON-tuh-SAWR-us

Parasaurolophus
PAR-ah-sawr-OL-oh-fus

DID YOU KNOW?

Scientists have found evidence of over 10,000 hadrosaur dinosaurs buried in one location in Montana.

Maiasaura
mah-ee-ah-SAWR-uh

Parasaurolophus and Iguanodon

*P*arasaurolophus ("near crested lizard"), a member of the Lambeosaurines, was up to 40 feet long and weighed around two tons. Since its back legs were much stronger than the front, it may have walked on four legs and run on two. It had no front teeth, only a broad, flat, toothless beak that resembled a duck-bill. It had hundreds of cheek teeth that could grind up tough vegetation. Stomachs of mummified specimens contain conifer needles, branches, twigs, seeds, fruit, and other coarse plants.

Iguanodon ("iguana tooth") was one of the earliest named dinosaurs. It was an herbivore that was about 30 feet long, weighed around three tons, and had four- to six-inch-long spikes on its front thumbs. It walked on all four legs but was capable of walking on only two. It probably held its head lower than its back, using its tail for balance. Perceptions of this large reptile have undergone many changes since it was first discovered.

CREST

Parasaurolophus possessed an iconic nasal crest on its head that initially caused much debate among scientists. Was it used as a kind of snorkel? A weapon? Eventually, they realized that it was actually constructed like a horn and decided it was probably used as a communication device, capable of emitting deep resounding blasts that echoed over the landscape.
Young *Parasaurolophus* had small bumps on their heads that eventually grew into these horn-like crests.

LAMBEOSAURINES

Some paleontologists place "crested lizards" into a subfamily called the Lambeosaurines. These dinosaurs were designed with a wide range of sound-making tubes and crests connected to their nasal cavities. The diversity in the shapes of the crests would have provided a different sound for each family unit, something like different brass instruments.

There is evidence that *Parasaurolophus* had at least partially webbed feet, so it may have lived in swampy areas. It probably traveled through these swamps in large herds, since it is commonly found with many other specimens of the same kind.

DID YOU KNOW?

Scientists have used skulls of the *Parasaurolophus* to reconstruct its horn-like call. Listen to it online!

Parasaurolophus
PAR-ah-sawr-OL-oh-fus

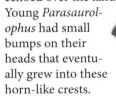

WHAT'S IN A NAME?

When the first *Iguanodon* fossil fragments were found in England in 1822, scientists initially thought they were from a rhinoceros. But discoverer Gideon Mantell eventually realized they came from a reptile. He compared his fossils with the skeleton of a modern iguana and saw that they were remarkably similar, except much larger. He theorized that the fossils came from an extinct reptile, named it *Iguanodon*, and published his conclusions in 1825.

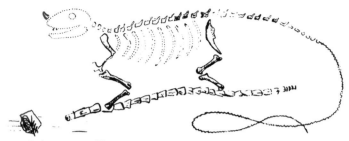

Gideon Mantell's inaccurate 1825 *Iguanodon* sketch

Iguanodon
ig-WAN-uh-DON

DID YOU KNOW?

Because *Iguanodon* was identified so early, a lot of dinosaurs discovered afterward were assigned to the *Iguanodon* group. Subsequent research has shown many of these dinosaurs don't belong there, but scientists are still trying to sort out which of them are *Iguanodon* and which aren't.

Iguanodon

Parasaurolophus

THE SPIKE

One of *Iguanodon*'s distinctive features is its thumb spike. The spike was originally thought to be located on its nose like a rhinoceros horn (see Mantell's drawing above). It wasn't until 1878 that a more complete specimen was found and the spike was put where it belonged—on the thumb. Scientists still aren't sure what its purpose was. The spikes might have been used as a defense against predators, or they could have helped *Iguanodon* forage for food.

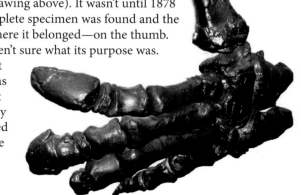

Dinosaurs in the Big Picture

Dinosaurs have fascinated people ever since their bones were first unearthed. But what is their true story? Did they evolve over millions of years and then go extinct long before humans arrived? Or were they created at the same time as humans and only died out recently, like the Bible indicates? As this book shows, the evidence best fits the biblical account.

WHERE DID DINOSAURS COME FROM?

God must have created dinosaurs. We know they didn't get here through evolution because dinosaurs had essential parts that could not be altered without killing them. If they had evolved to or from another creature, the in-between features would have reshaped these essential parts, resulting in a transitional creature that would have died. Plus, each dinosaur kind appears in the fossil record as a fully formed creature, with no evidence of evolutionary tinkering.

"For in six days the LORD made the heavens and the earth, the sea, and all that is in them, and rested the seventh day. Therefore the LORD blessed the Sabbath day and hallowed it." (Exodus 20:11)

FOSSILS FROM A FLOOD

Dinosaur fossils mystify secular scientists, who struggle to explain how ancient streams or rivers could have overwhelmed and buried them. If that happened in the past, then why don't today's river floods make huge deposits of fossils? In contrast, Scripture describes a year-long global flood that occurred about 1,600 years after creation. This generated the forces and terrible conditions needed to fossilize dinosaurs and other creatures on every continent.

NOAH'S ARK AND DINOSAUR SURVIVAL

Genesis 7:22 says that during the Flood, "all in whose nostrils was the breath of the spirit of life, all that was on the dry land, died." Fossils show that dinosaurs had nostrils. Therefore, they all died in the Flood, except the two of every kind taken onto the Ark. There were about 60 basic dinosaur kinds, totaling 120 or so dinosaurs—probably smaller juveniles—that would have occupied a small section on one of the Ark's three decks.

DINOSAUR EXTINCTION

Dinosaurs lived after the Flood. They likely thrived in the Middle East during the Ice Age, when that region was lush and tropical instead of dry and dusty like today. The many droughts recorded in Genesis signaled losses of tropical habitats. These post-Flood climate and atmospheric changes along with dinosaur hunting—every culture has legends of dragon slayers—eventually drove dinosaurs to extinction.

SOFT TISSUES

Aren't dinosaur bones supposed to be millions of years old? Some contain soft tissues like blood vessels, as well as proteins and DNA. Lab experiments show that although these kinds of molecules can last up to thousands of years, they would certainly disappear before a million years elapsed. According to Scripture, the Flood occurred about 4,500 years ago. So dinosaur soft tissues fit the timeframe of the Genesis Flood.

A DINOSAUR IN THE BIBLE

Do dinosaurs appear in the Bible? Job lived in the Middle East about 350 years after the Flood, during the Ice Age. God told him to "look now" at a creature called behemoth (Job 40:15). Was it a dinosaur? It was the "first of the ways of God," which could mean it was the largest creature God made. Fossils show that the largest land animals were sauropods. Behemoth was so big that though "the river may rage, yet he is not disturbed," and "he moves his tail like a cedar." Some dinosaurs certainly had tree-size tails.

WHAT DINOSAURS MEAN TO ME

The clearest lesson dinosaur fossils teach us is that God takes sin so seriously that He once sent a global flood that destroyed every land creature and human except for those saved in the Ark. The Lord promises a future judgment. People will have no more chance of saving themselves than dinosaurs did from the Flood. The good news is that God provides a Savior in the person of His Son. When we trust that Jesus' death paid our sin penalty and believe that God raised Jesus from the dead, He saves us from the coming judgment and provides eternal life with Him. Just as Noah's family was saved in the Ark, each of us should make sure we have placed ourselves in Christ, the life-saving Creator.

"For I delivered to you first of all that which I also received: that Christ died for our sins according to the Scriptures, and that He was buried, and that He rose again the third day according to the Scriptures."
(1 Corinthians 15: 3-4)

Index

Contributors

BRIAN THOMAS, M.S., ICR SCIENCE WRITER

Brian Thomas received his bachelor's degree in biology from Stephen F. Austin State University (1993). He earned a master's degree in biotechnology in 1999 also from Stephen F. Austin State University. He taught biology at the high school level and biology, chemistry, and anatomy at the college level. Mr. Thomas is the Science Writer at ICR, where he is responsible for contributing news and magazine articles, editing, and speaking on creation issues, as well as researching original tissue fossils. He is the author of *Dinosaurs and the Bible* and presents compelling dinosaur information in the DVD *What You Haven't Been Told about Dinosaurs.*

TIM CLAREY, PH.D., ICR RESEARCH ASSOCIATE

Dr. Tim Clarey received a bachelor's degree in geology from Western Michigan University (1982), a master's degree in geology from the University of Wyoming (1984), a master's degree in hydrogeology from Western Michigan University (1993), and a Ph.D. in geology from Western Michigan University (1996). Dr. Clarey worked as an exploration geologist with Chevron USA, Inc., and he served as professor and geosciences chair at the college level for 17 years before joining the ICR science staff. He participated in several dinosaur digs in Wyoming and Montana, using these experiences to create an undergraduate class on the science of dinosaurs that he taught for over a decade. He has written peer-reviewed papers on dinosaurs and the geology of the Rocky Mountains and authored three college laboratory books.

Acknowledgements

Special thanks to Graphic Designer Susan Windsor for contributing her artistic expertise in the creation of *Guide to Dinosaurs*. In addition to the graphic design and layout of this book, she utilized her watercolor painting experience in illustrating many of these dinosaur images. By consulting with the book's contributors, she was able to represent these dinosaurs in an artistic yet accurate way.

Thanks, too, to Senior Editor Beth Mull for combing through the fine details to confirm the accuracy of the dinosaur data and to present technical information in reader-friendly terms. Editors Michael Stamp and Truett Billups also provided helpful reviews. We're grateful for the opportunity to serve at the Institute for Creation Research, and we appreciate Dr. Henry Morris III's continued dedication to his father's mission. As CEO, Dr. Morris provides the leadership and vision to reach others with the biblical truths of creation. Sharing the creation message with you, our readers, is a privilege. In *Guide to Dinosaurs,* we hope you will experience anew the wonder of His marvelous works!

Jayme Durant, Executive Editor

Susan Windsor

Jayme Durant

Image Credits

t-top; m-middle; b-bottom; c-center; l-left; r-right

Ballista (Wikipedia): 111br

Bigstock: 8-10, 12bl,br, 13tl,tr,m-l,mr,br, 14b, 15, 16b, 17-18, 19tl,tr,b, 21ml, 22t, 23, 24ml, 26br, 27-28, 29b, 30r, 31l, 34tl, 35tl,tr, 36-37m, 38tr, 39bl, 41tr,mb, 48b, 49br, 51b, 52bl,br, 54, 55tr,bl,br, 56tl,tm,tr,ml,b, 57-58, 59tl,ml,bl, 60bl, 62, 63tr, 64-65, 66br, 67b, 68t,m; 69b, 70, 71tr,m, 72b, 73b, 74tl,br, 76bl, 77tr,mr,bm,br, 78, 79tr,m,mr,br, 80tl,r,bl, 81m, 82m,br, 83bl,br, 84tr, 85ml,mr,br, 86r, 87l,tr,ml,b, 88r, 89tl,bl,br, 90b, 91tr,mr,b, 93-94, 95ml,br, 97br, 98r, 99tl,br, 101tr,br, 102tl, 103mr,b, 104r, 105t,m, 106r, 107mr,mb,br, 108-109b, 110t, 111bl, 112t, 113

Allie Caulfield (Wikipedia): 102r-103l

The Childrens Museum of Indianapolis (Wikipedia): 37br, 97tr, 100

Tim Clarey: 30l, 35b, 76-77m, 77tl, 81tl,tr, 82bl, 87tl, 90tr

Dinosaur National Monument: 26tl,bl, 43tr,tm, 112b

Fotolia: 11t, 21c, 22b, 32-33, 48tr, 55tl, 59tr, 69m, 74tm,tr,bl, 83t, 92, 96br, 107t, 111ml

Jens L. Franzen, Philip D. Gingerich, Jörg Habersetzer1, Jørn H. Hurum, Wighart von Koenigswald, B. Holly Smith (Wikipedia): 31tr

FunkMonk (Wikipedia): 88tl, 89tr,mr, 96tl

Ghedoghedo (Wikipedia): 90tl

Jakub Halun (Wikipedia): 25tr

Claire Houck (Wikipedia): 101tl

ICR: 16t, 19m, 22m, 43tl, 46-47, 50tr, 51tr,m, 67tr, 108l

iStock: 13bl, 16m, 25br, 34bl,br, 39c, 41bl, 42bl, 49mr, 51tl, 53bl, 56mc, 61tr, 81bl, 84br, 97bl, 104l

Eva K. (Wikipedia): 63ml

Lentus (Wikipedia): 41mr

John Morris: 20bl, 21t,b, 71b

Vance Nelson: 44mr,ml,bc,br,rbm

Pacific Northwest National Laboratory: 50bl

Jordi Paya (Wikipedia): 95tr

PLoS: 52-53t

Public Domain: 12t,ml, 13ml, 24tr, 25ml, 36tr, 38tl,br, 39ml,tr,br, 40, 42tr, 43br,bl, 48ml, 49tr, 60br, 66tl,tr, 82t, 83m, 84l, 85tl,tr, 88bl, 96bl, 99tr,

101bl, 102bl, 106bl, 111tr

Daryl Robbins: 24br, 45tr

ScottRobertAnselmo (WIkipedia): 86l

Smokeybjb (Wikipedia): 75b

TadekKurpaski (Wikipedia): 91tl

Yuya Tamai (Wikipedia): 59br

Brian Thomas: 14t, 20tr, 29t,tr, 44tr,tl, 45tl,b, 63br

Eduard Sola Vazquez (Wikipedia): 75m, 79bl

Wilson44691 (Wikipedia): 98bl

Susan Windsor: 11b, 20br, 31br, 38bl, 39tl, 49bl, 60t, 61bl,m,br, 68b, 69t, 72t, 73t,m, 80br, 87mr, 105tr,ml,b, 107ml, 109tl,tr, 110b, 111tl

About the Institute for Creation Research

After more than four decades of ministry, the Institute for Creation Research remains a leader in scientific research within the context of biblical creation. Founded by Dr. Henry Morris in 1970, ICR exists to conduct scientific research within the realms of origins and Earth history and then to educate the public both formally and informally through graduate and professional training programs, through conferences and seminars around the country, and through books, magazines, and media presentations. ICR was established for three main purposes:

Dr. Henry Morris

Research. ICR conducts laboratory, field, theoretical, and library research on projects that seek to understand the science of origins and Earth history. ICR scientists have conducted multi-year research projects at key locations such as Grand Canyon, Mount St. Helens, Yosemite Valley, Santa Cruz River Valley in Argentina, and on vital issues like Radioisotopes and the Age of the Earth (RATE), Flood-Activated Sedimentation and Tectonics (FAST), the human genome, and other topics related to geology, genetics, astro/geophysics, paleo-climatology, and much more.

Education. ICR offers formal courses of instruction and conducts seminars and workshops, as well as other means of instruction. With 30 years of experience in graduate education, first through our California-based science education program (1981-2010), and now through the degree programs at the School of Biblical Apologetics, ICR trains men and women to do real-world apologetics with a foundation of biblical authority and creation science. ICR also offers a one-year, non-degree training program for professionals called the Creationist Worldview. Additionally, ICR scientists and staff speak to over 200 groups each year through seminars and conferences.

Communication. ICR produces books, videos, periodicals, and other media for communicating the evidence and information related to its research and education. ICR's central publication is *Acts & Facts*, a free full-color monthly magazine with a readership of over 250,000, providing articles relevant to science, apologetics, education, and worldview issues. ICR also publishes the daily devotional *Days of Praise* with over 300,000 subscribers worldwide. Our website at www.icr.org features regular and relevant creation science updates. The three radio programs produced by ICR can be heard on outlets around the world.

Founded in southern California but now headquartered in Dallas, Texas, the Institute for Creation Research continues to expand its work and influence in each of these areas of ministry, endeavoring to encourage Christians with the wonders of God's creation.

INSTITUTE FOR
CREATION
RESEARCH

P. O. Box 59029
Dallas, Texas 75229
www.icr.org

800.337.0375 (main) | 800.628.7640 (customer service)

Get more facts with *Guide to Creation Basics* and *Guide to Animals*!
Designed for all ages, these hardcover books are loaded with cutting-edge
scientific information and hundreds of full-color illustrations.

To order, call **800.628.7640** or visit **www.icr.org/store**

Also available for Kindle, Nook, and through the iBookstore